STECK-VAUGHN

BOOK 1

Entry to English Literacy

A Real-Life Approach

Author

Kathleen Kelley Beal

Reviewers

Beth Powell
Literacy Specialist
Houston Community College

Kathleen Santopietro
Consultant, Adult Basic Education
Colorado Department of Education

STECK-VAUGHN
C O M P A N Y
A Subsidiary of National Education Corporation

Acknowledgments

About the Author

Kathleen Kelley Beal is an experienced educator in the field of English as a Second Language. She has taught ESL at the University of Colorado, in Boulder, Colorado, at Fort Steilacoom Community College in Tacoma, Washington, and at Mott Community College in Flint, Michigan. She has served as consultant and presenter at many ESL workshops and conferences and is the author of *Speaking of Pictures,* a conversation-oriented program for adult ESL students.

Photography

Cover: Crowd, © Paul Henning/UNIPHOTO; Street, © Richard Laird/FPG

Inside Photography:
Rick Williams
Phyllis Liedeker
Stan Kearl

Except:Texas Highways, (p.11 speed limit); Bill Records (p.11 30 mph); Cynthia Ellis (p.13 vet); Jerry Jones (p.13 grocery checkout) Bob Daemmerich (p.14 all, 18 van, 72 roses, 88 male, 89 Mr. & Mrs. Gonzalez) Rick Patrick (p.17 father & children, 20 bus stop, 62 no smoking, p.90) Sandy Wilson (pp.17,18 family) Craig Jobson (p.21 monkey bars); © Tony Freeman/PhotoEdit (p.21 team); R. David Taylor, Jr. (p.29 pencil); Jamaica Tourist Board (p.36 Jamaica book); Texas Parks & Wildlife (p.36 dolphin); Scott Huber (p.36 elephant); NASA (p.36 space book); South Carolina Department of Highways (p.57 east, 72 Riverbanks Zoo); Singer Sewing Notions (p.57 safety pins); Alfonso Barrios (p.57 dog, 63 bike lane); U.S. Postal Service (p.88 female); © Michal Heron (p.88 inspector); R. David Taylor (p.89); Jim Myers (p.89 Miss Jones); © FourByFive/Superstock (p. 115 house fire); © DPI (p. 115 car accident) ; Los Angeles City Fire Department (p.123 fire fighters).

Illustration

Linda Butler
Sue Durban

Staff Credits

Supervising Editor: Carolyn M. Hall
Senior Editor: Beverly A. Grossman
Cover Design: Joyce Spicer

ISBN 0-8114-4633-6

Contents

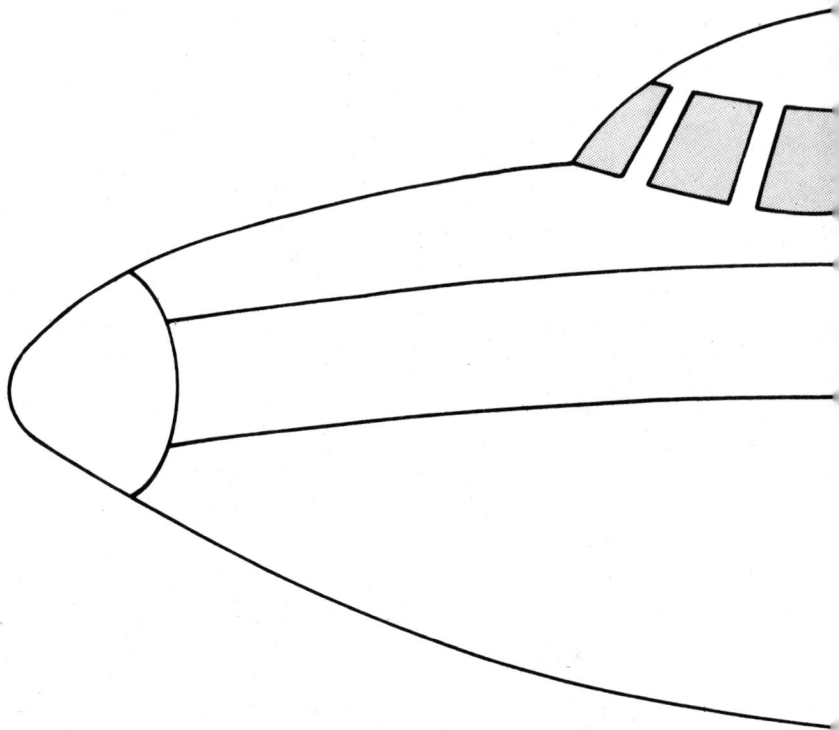

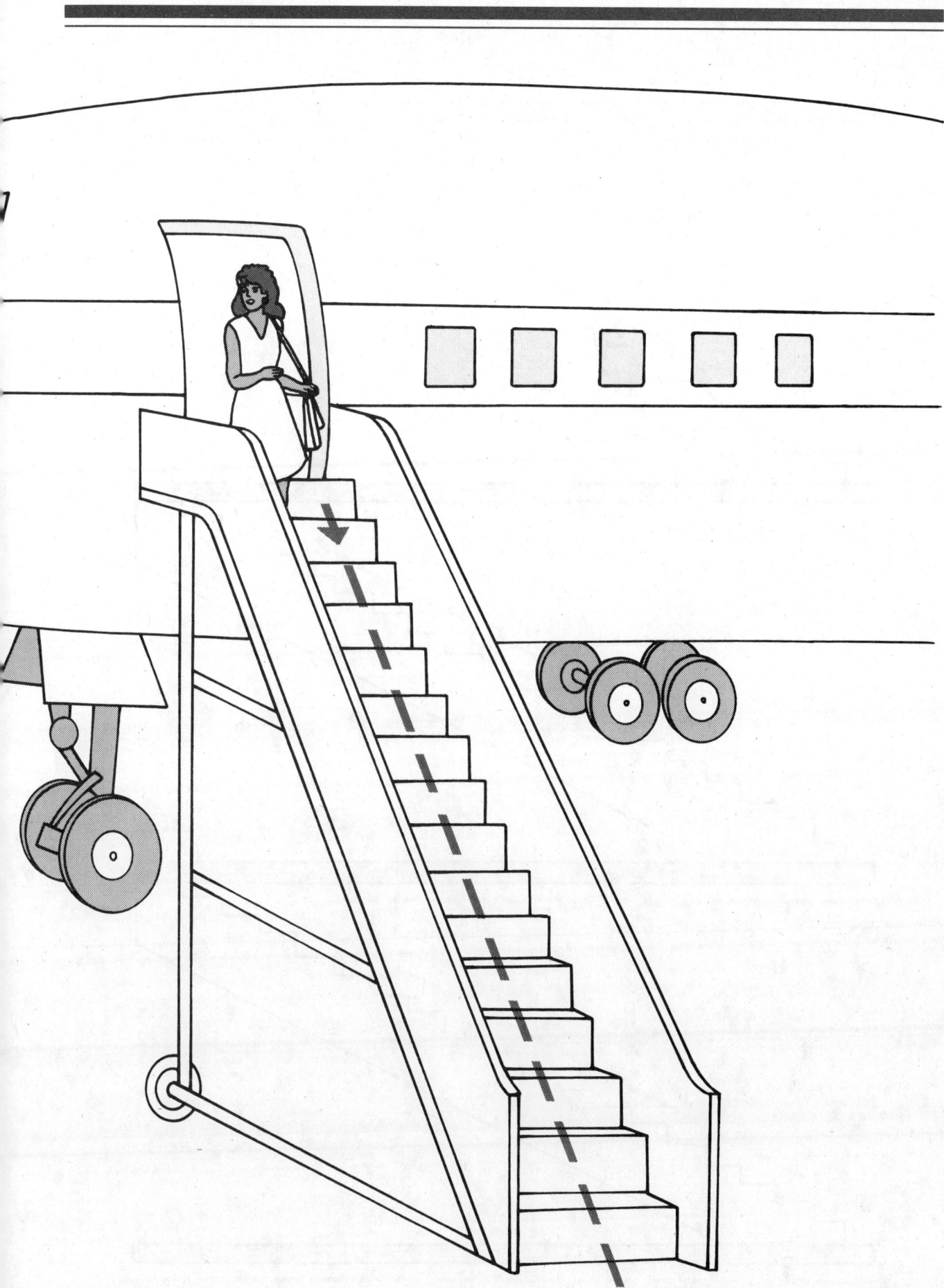

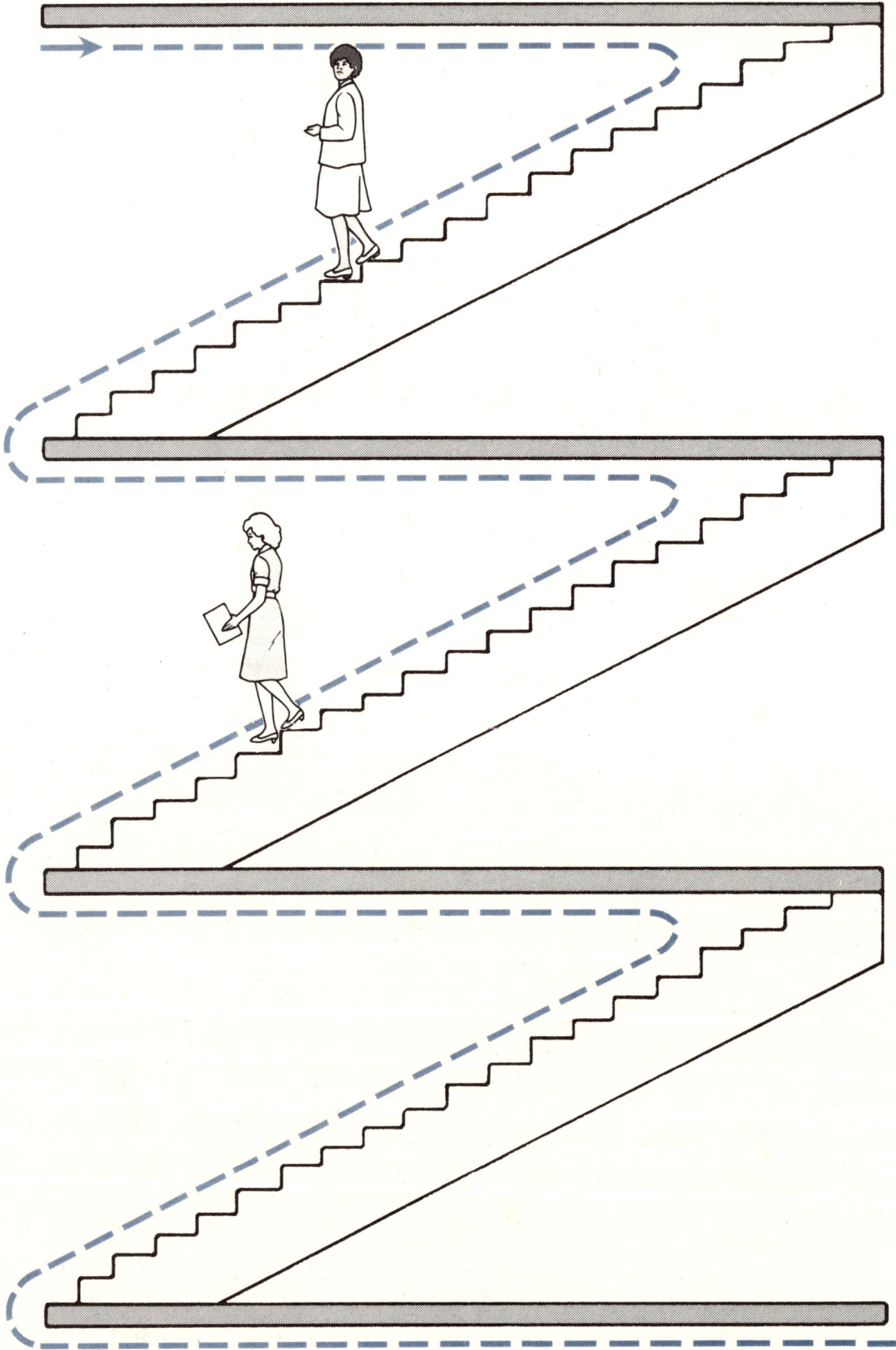

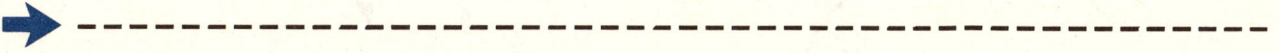

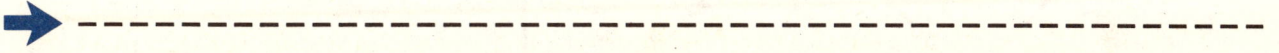

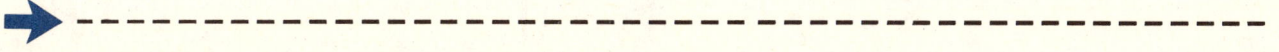

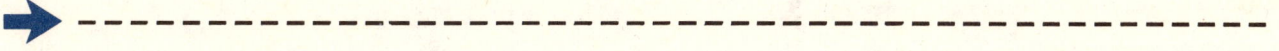

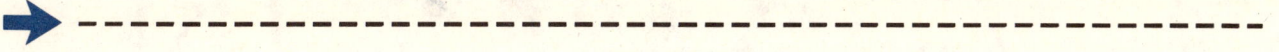

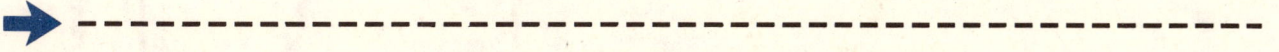

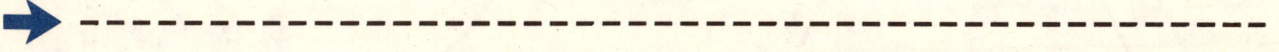

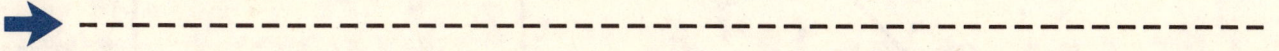

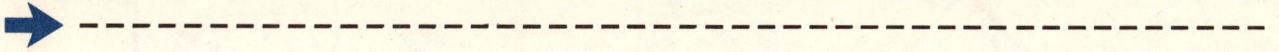

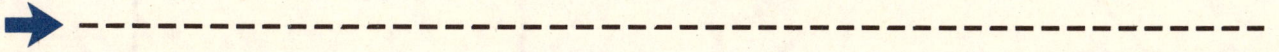

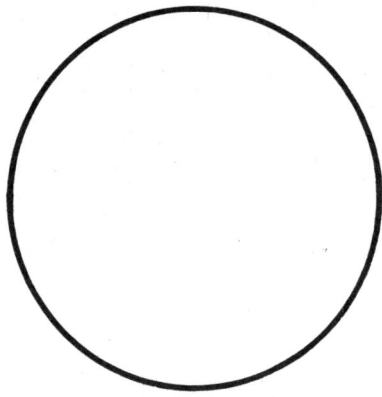
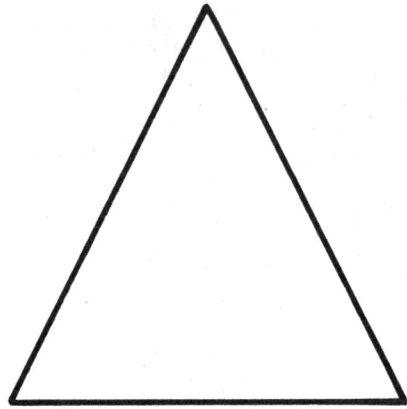
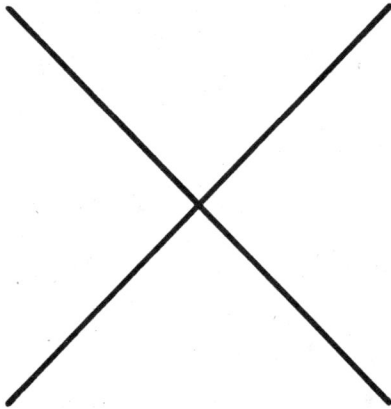
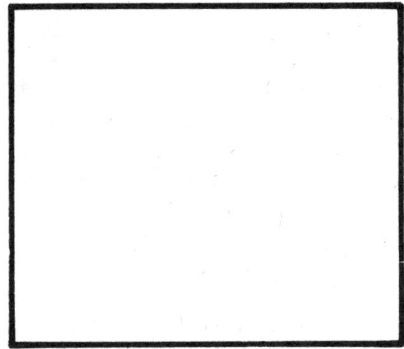
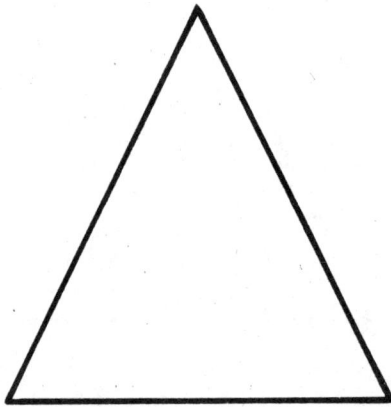
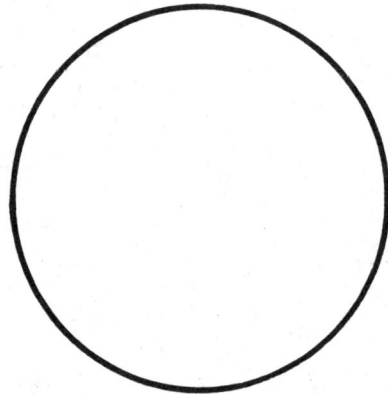
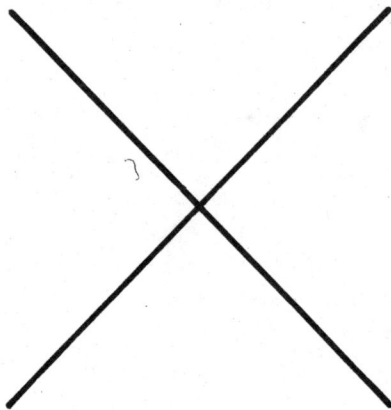

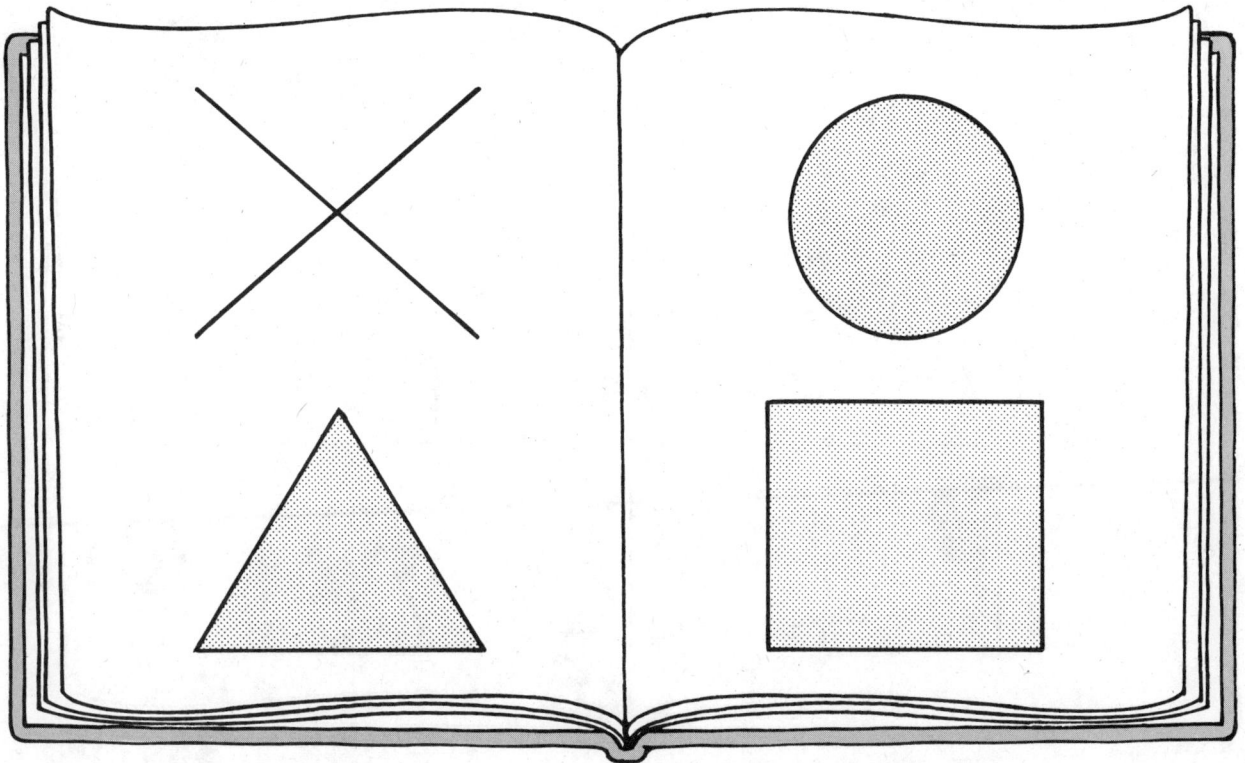

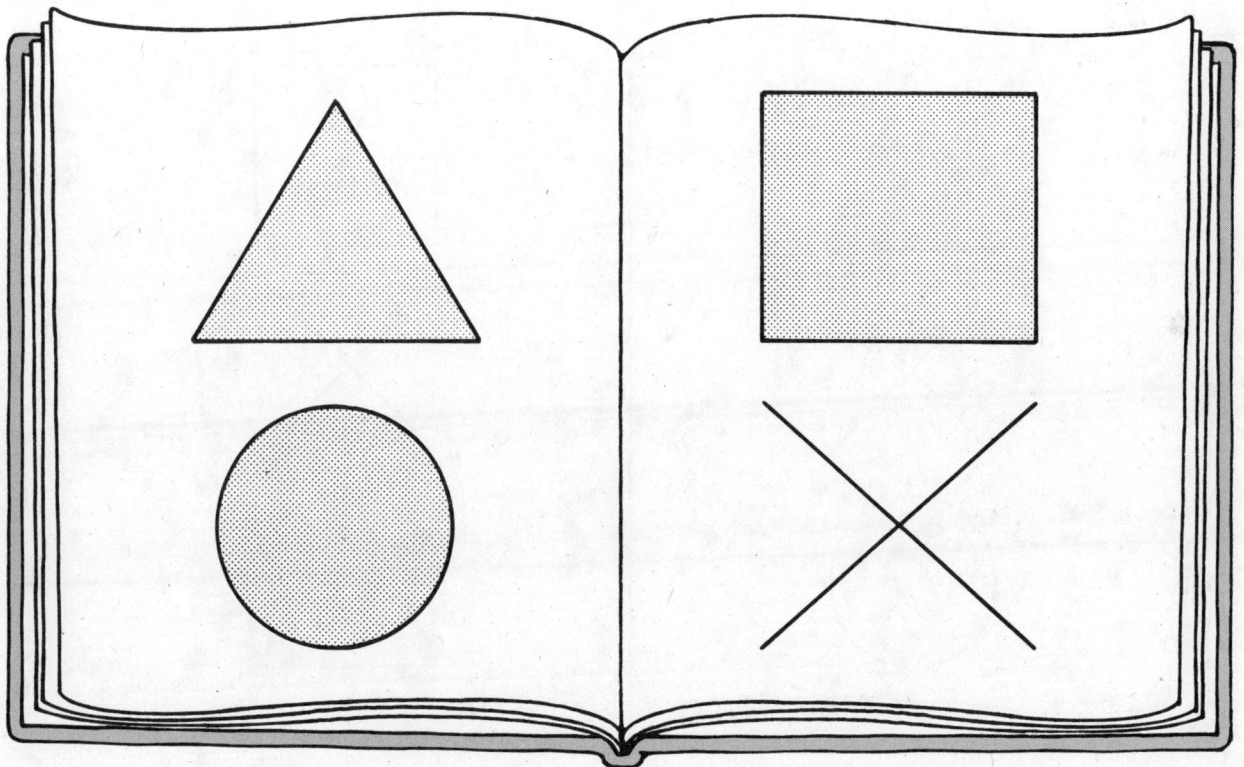

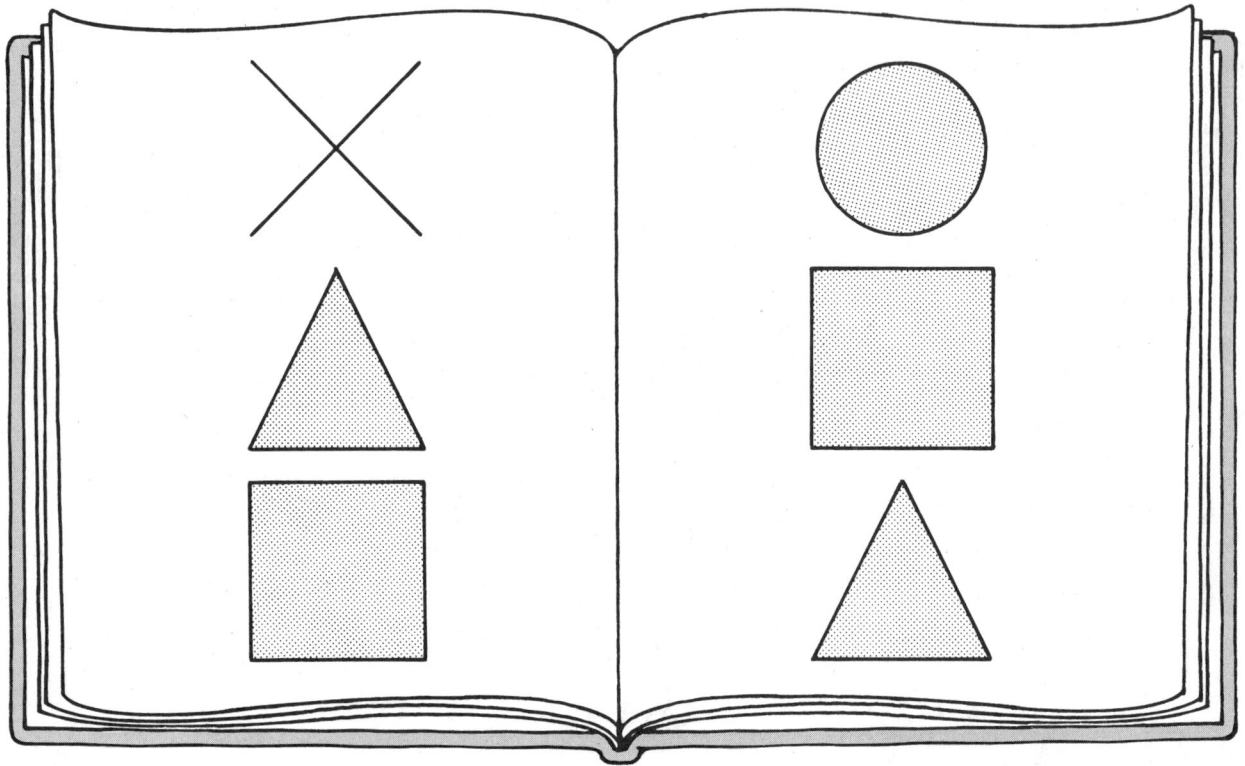

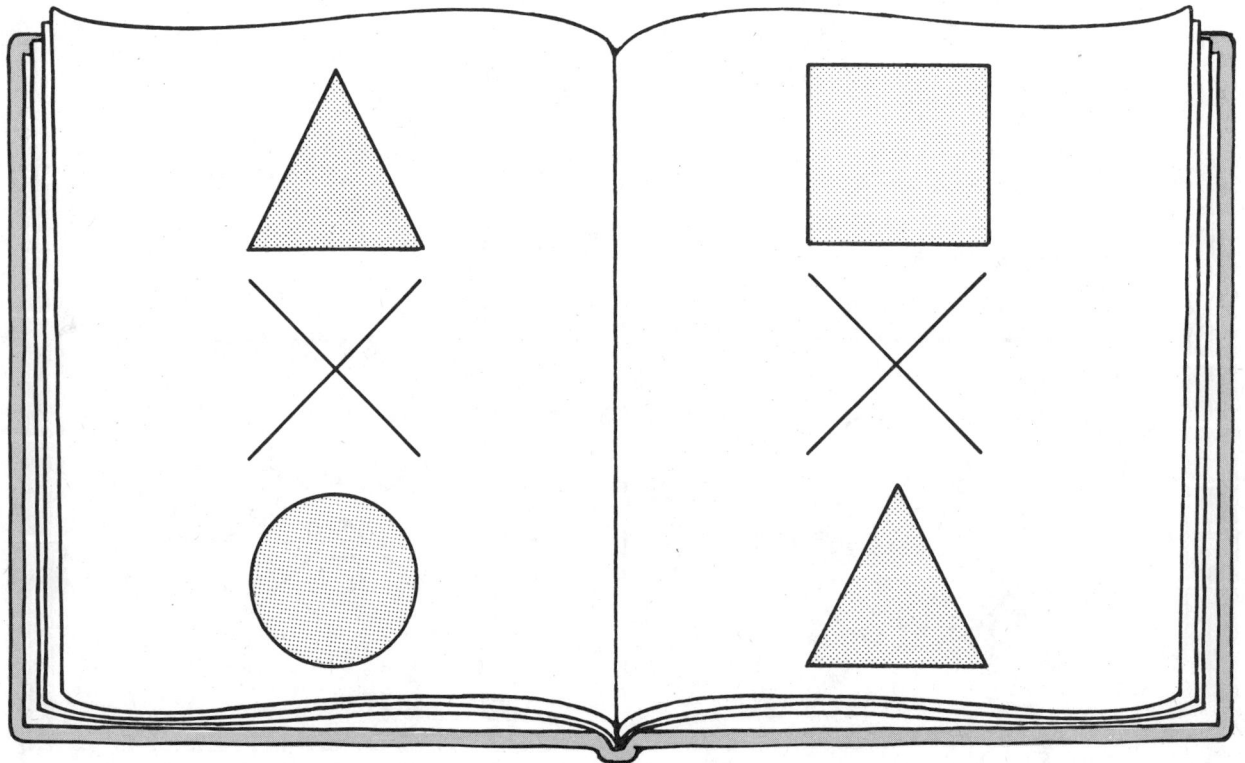

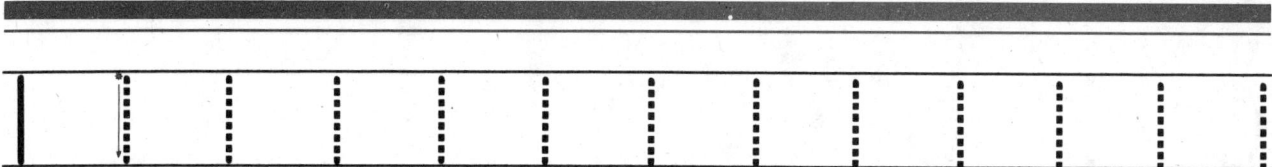

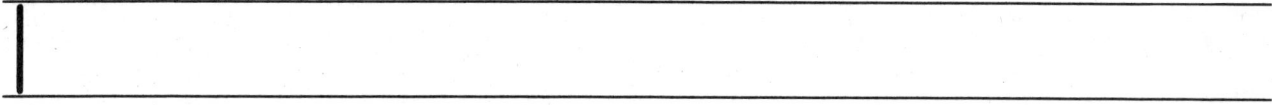

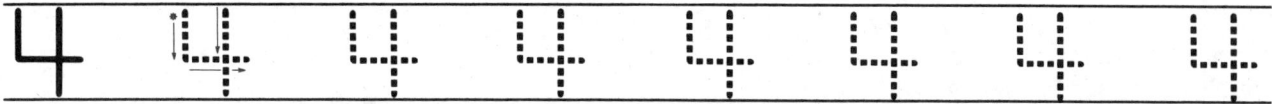

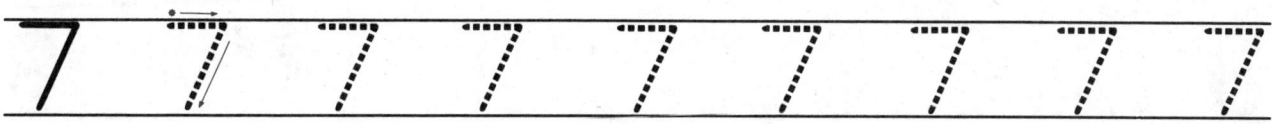

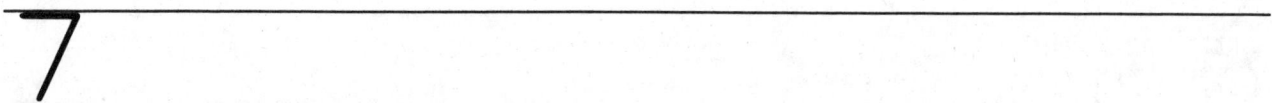

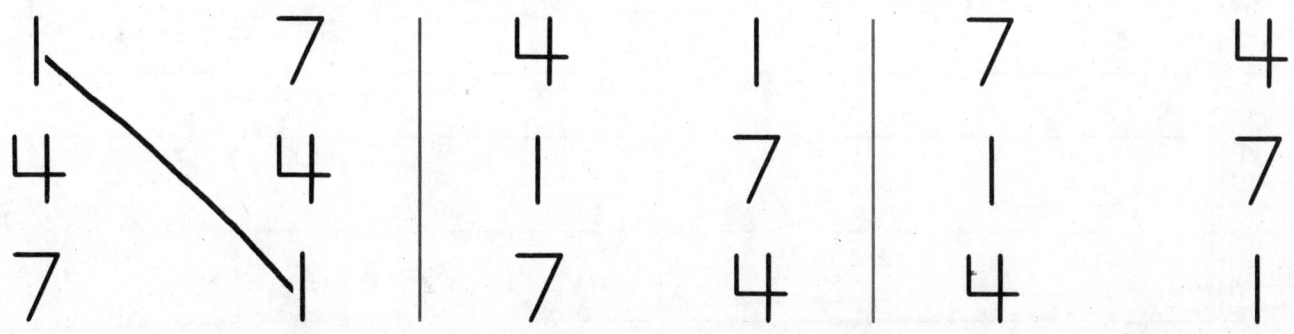

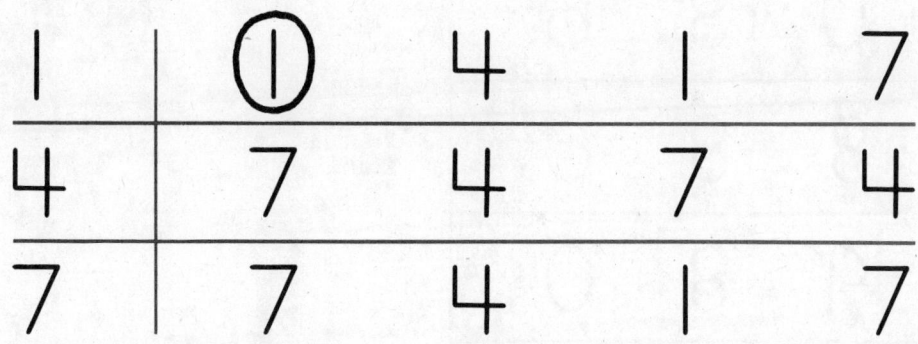

0 0 0 0 0 0 0 0 0

0

6 6 6 6 6 6 6 6 6

6

8 8 8 8 8 8 8 8 8

8

9 9 9 9 9 9 9 9 9

9

0	8	0	6	0
6	6	0	8	6
8	9	8	8	6
9	6	9	8	0

2 2 2 2 2 2 2 2 2 2

2

3 3 3 3 3 3 3 3 3 3

3

5 5 5 5 5 5 5 5 5 5

5

2	3	5	2	3	5
3	5	3	5	5	2
5	2	2	3	2	3

2	3	2	5	2
3	2	3	2	5
5	5	2	5	3

14	14	41	44	14
71	17	71	71	11
98	99	88	98	98
147	117	147	147	717
908	908	980	999	980
777	711	177	777	117
601	106	666	601	601

68 ___ ___ ___ ___

23 ___ ___ ___ ___

54 ___ ___ ___ ___

896 ___ ___ ___ ___

523 ___ ___ ___ ___

673 ___ ___ ___ ___

_____

_____

_____

_____

_____

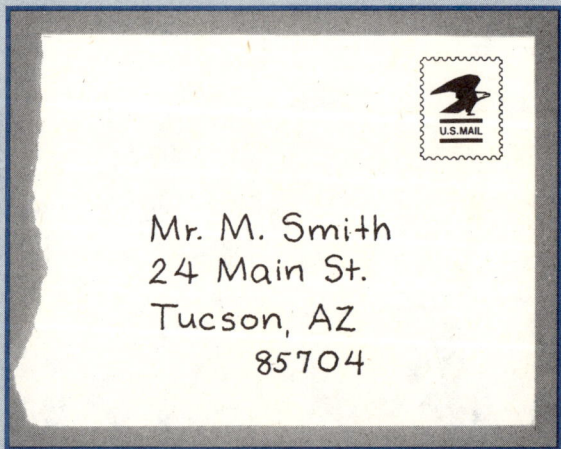

_____

| 1 |  |

1

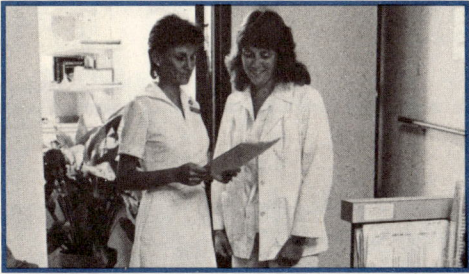

2

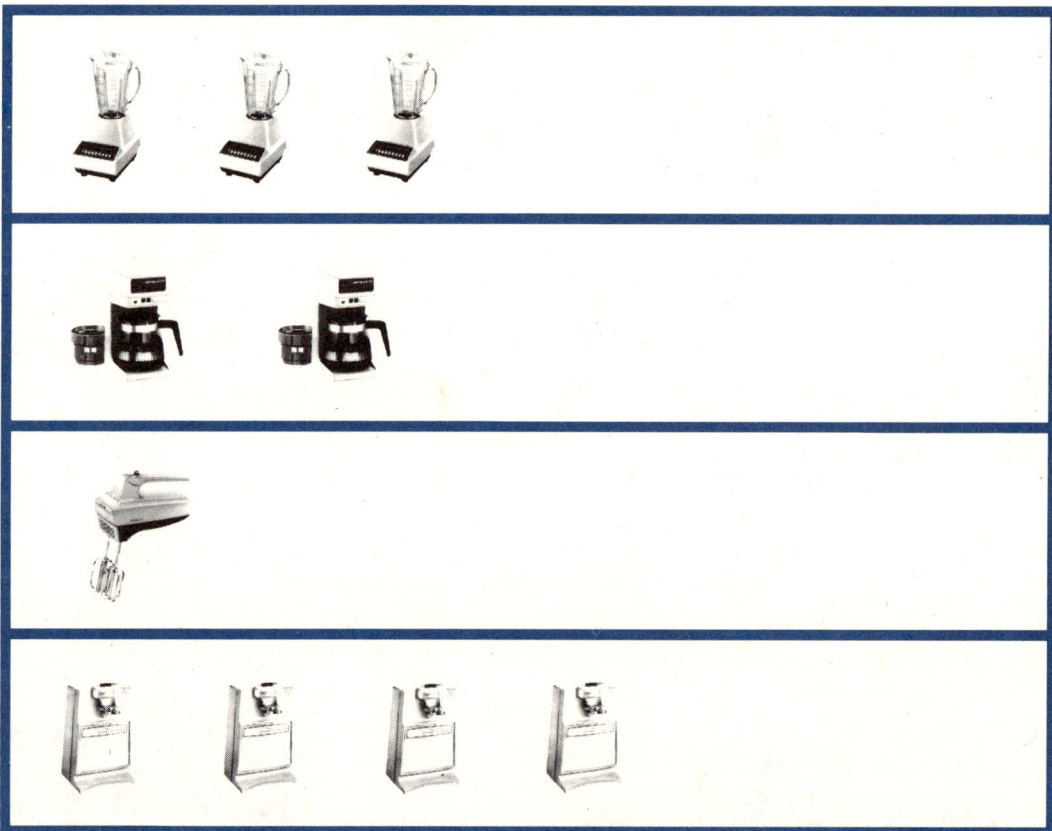

1

2

1   2   3   4   5   6   7   8   9

▲   ▲   ▲

3   🪑 🪑 🪑

2

1

3

15

1 2 3 4 5 6 7 8 9

▲ ▲ ▲ ▲

4

2

1

3

4

16

1　2　3　4　5　6　7　8　9

▲　▲　▲　▲　▲

| 5 |  |

2	
4	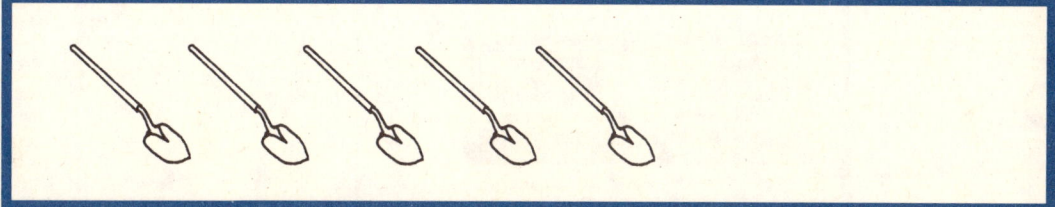
5	
3	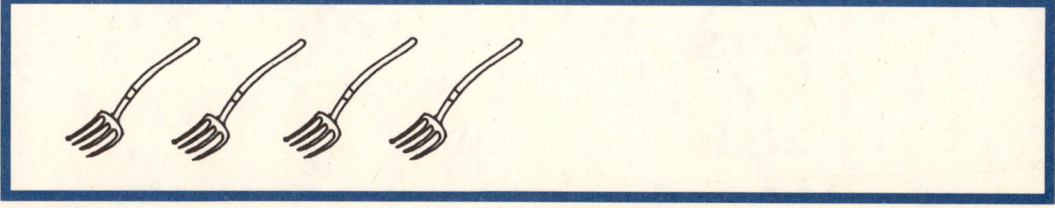

3　1　5

3　1　5

6

6

5

1

2

4 5 6

4 5 6

7

7

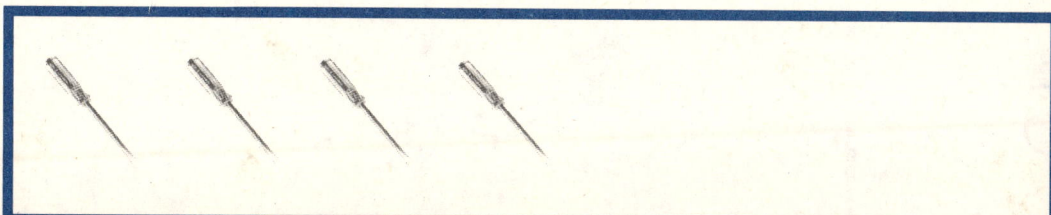

4

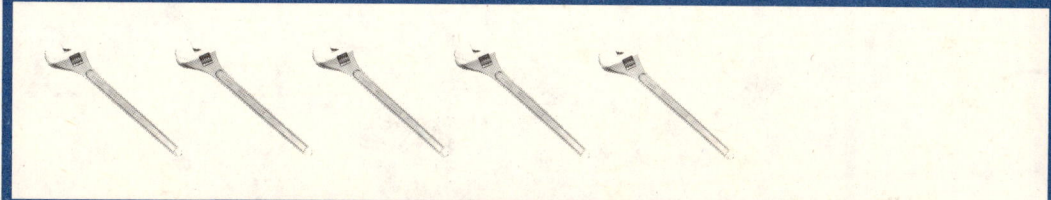

5

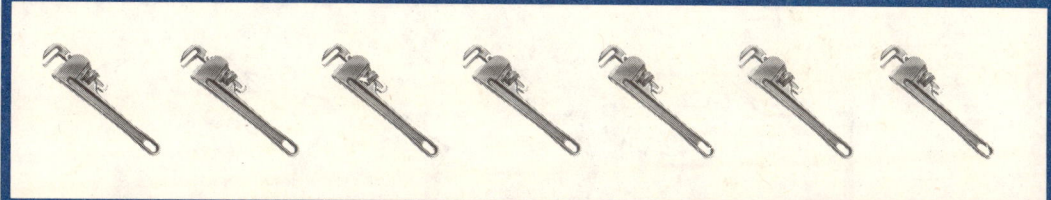

1

1 2 3 4 5 6 7 8 9

▲ ▲ ▲ ▲ ▲ ▲ ▲ ▲

| 8 |  |

5

7

8

4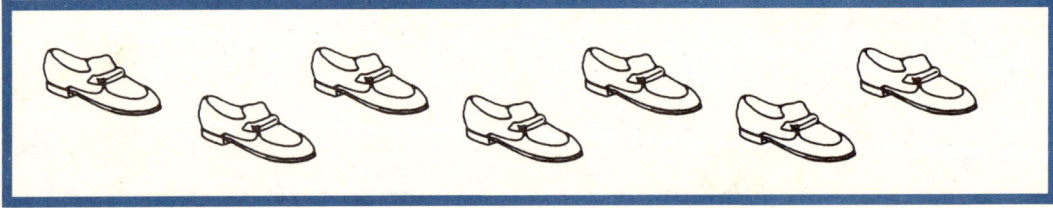

3   4   8

3   4   8

1　2　3　4　5　6　7　8　9

▲　▲　▲　▲　▲　▲　▲　▲　▲

9	

5

9

7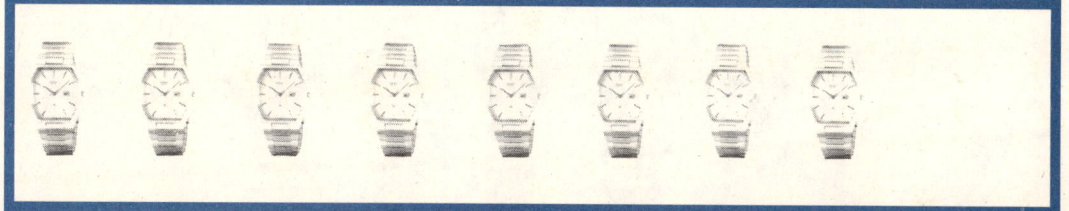

8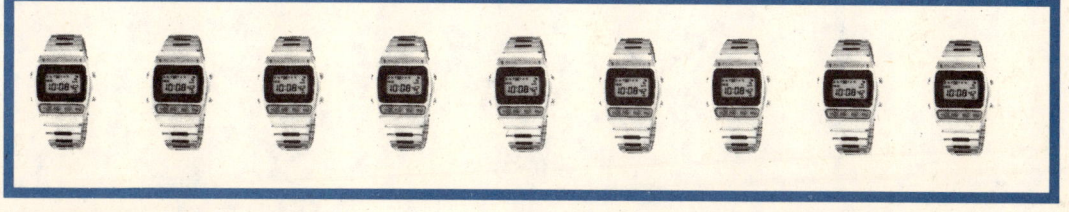

6　8　9

6　8　9

21

0

5

0

3

1

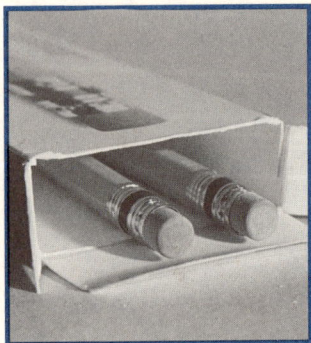

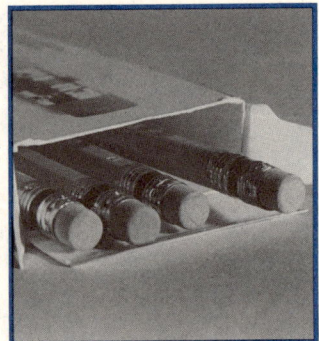

0 2 4   0 2 4   0 2 4

1   2   3   4   5   6   7   8   9   10

▲   ▲   ▲   ▲   ▲   ▲   ▲   ▲   ▲   ▲

11   12   13   14   15   16   17   18   19   20

10

8

6

10

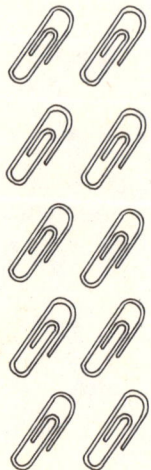  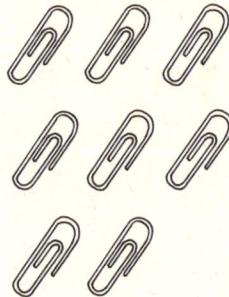 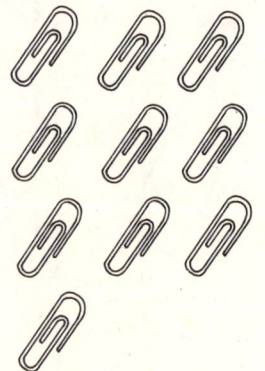

24

1 2 3 4 5 6 7 8 9 10
▲ ▲ ▲ ▲ ▲ ▲ ▲ ▲ ▲ ▲
11 12 13 14 15 16 17 18 19 20
▲

| 11 |  |

8

11

6

  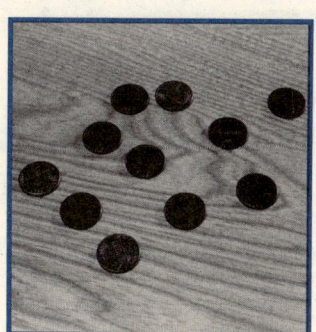

1   2   3   4   5   6   7   8   9   10

▲   ▲   ▲   ▲   ▲   ▲   ▲   ▲   ▲   ▲

11   12   13   14   15   16   17   18   19   20

▲   ▲

12

8

10

12

1	2	3	4	5	6	7	8	9	10
▲	▲	▲	▲	▲	▲	▲	▲	▲	▲
11	12	13	14	15	16	17	18	19	20
▲	▲	▲							

13

8

5

10

1 2 3 4 5 6 7 8 9 10
▲ ▲ ▲ ▲ ▲ ▲ ▲ ▲ ▲ ▲

11 12 13 14 15 16 17 18 19 20
▲ ▲ ▲ ▲

14

10

14

9

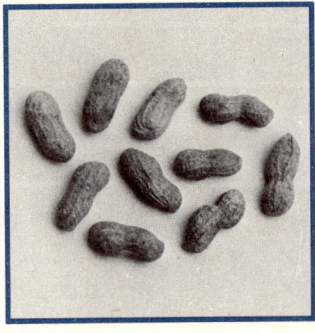

1 2 3 4 5 6 7 8 9 10
▲ ▲ ▲ ▲ ▲ ▲ ▲ ▲ ▲ ▲

11 12 13 14 15 16 17 18 19 20
▲ ▲ ▲ ▲ ▲

15 ///////////////

15

11

13

1 2 3 4 5 6 7 8 9 10

▲ ▲ ▲ ▲ ▲ ▲ ▲ ▲ ▲ ▲

11 12 13 14 15 16 17 18 19 20

▲ ▲ ▲ ▲ ▲ ▲

16

16

10

14

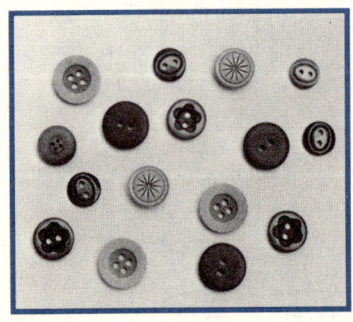

15 16 13

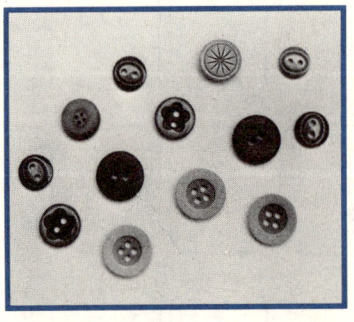

15 16 13

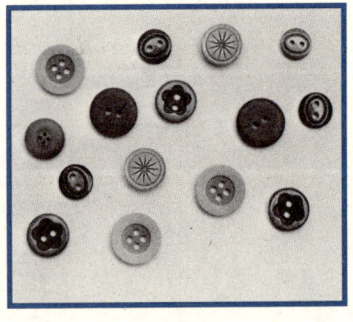

15 16 13

1	2	3	4	5	6	7	8	9	10
▲	▲	▲	▲	▲	▲	▲	▲	▲	▲

11	12	13	14	15	16	17	18	19	20
▲	▲	▲	▲	▲	▲	▲			

17

10

17

14

1 2 3 4 5 6 7 8 9 10
▲ ▲ ▲ ▲ ▲ ▲ ▲ ▲ ▲ ▲
11 12 13 14 15 16 17 18 19 20
▲ ▲ ▲ ▲ ▲ ▲ ▲ ▲

18

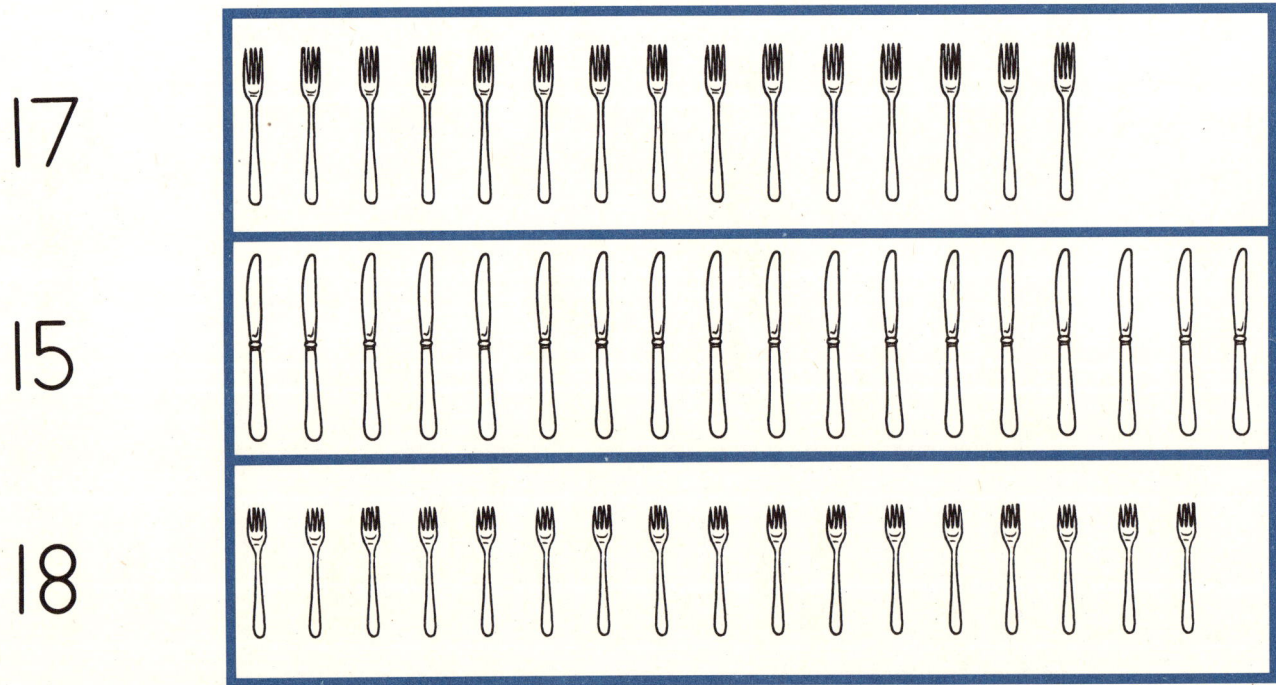

17

15

18

15   10   18

15   10   18

1 ▲ 2 ▲ 3 ▲ 4 ▲ 5 ▲ 6 ▲ 7 ▲ 8 ▲ 9 ▲ 10 ▲

11 ▲ 12 ▲ 13 ▲ 14 ▲ 15 ▲ 16 ▲ 17 ▲ 18 ▲ 19 ▲ 20

19

15

19

12

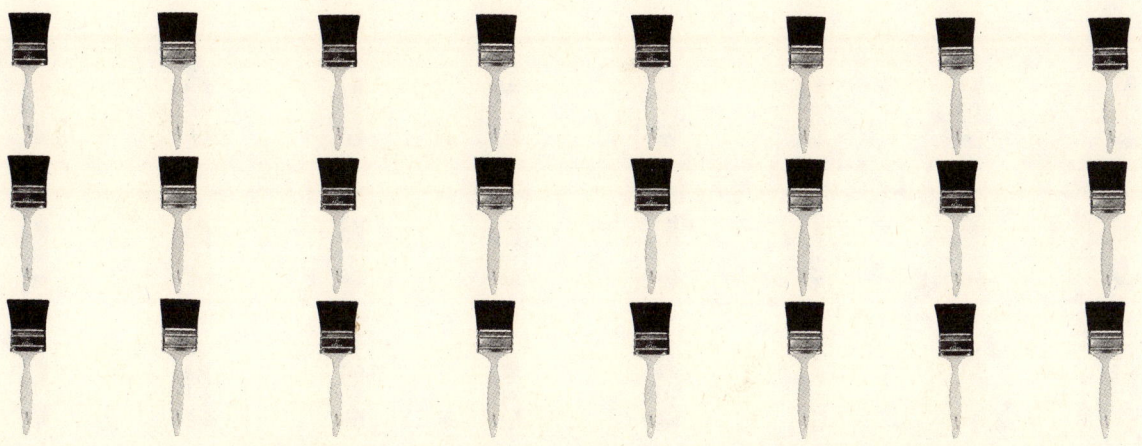

1　2　3　4　5　6　7　8　9　10
▲　▲　▲　▲　▲　▲　▲　▲　▲　▲

11　12　13　14　15　16　17　18　19　20
▲　▲　▲　▲　▲　▲　▲　▲　▲　▲

20

20

0

14

1 ___   6 ___   15 ___   11 ___

4 ___   9 ___   2 ___   18 ___

3 ___   10 ___   14 ___   17 ___

5 ___   7 ___   8 ___   12 ___

6 ___   13 ___   16 ___   19 ___

___ 6   ___ 9   ___ 20   ___ 16

___ 5   ___ 2   ___ 11   ___ 14

___ 13   ___ 16   ___ 19   ___ 10

___ 3   ___ 7   ___ 12   ___ 15

___ 4   ___ 8   ___ 17   ___ 18

3   15   5

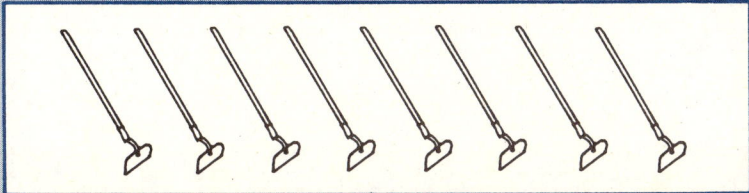

8   10   9

10   0   1

_____

_____

_____

_____

12 ___ 13 ___ 15 ___ 1 ___

5 ___ 7 ___ 10 ___ 5 ___

6 ___ 19 ___ 14 ___ 11 ___

___ 14 ___ 9 ___ 7 ___ 3

___ 1 ___ 6 ___ 12 ___ 8

___ 4 ___ 2 ___ 20 ___ 10

13 ___ ___ 15 2 ___ 19 ___

___ 7 8 ___ 9 ___ ___ 17

___ 18 19 ___ ___ 14 ___ 13

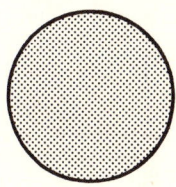 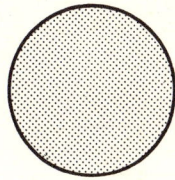  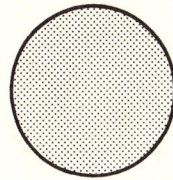 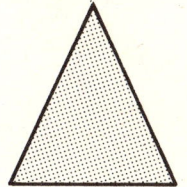

 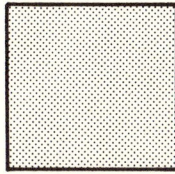   

 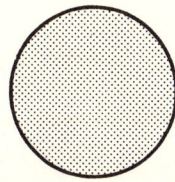   

    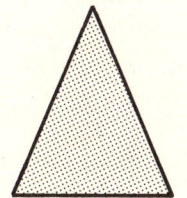

    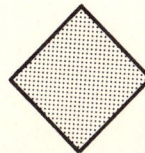 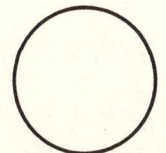

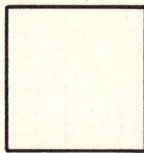

    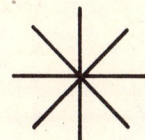 

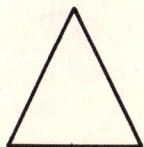 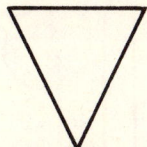 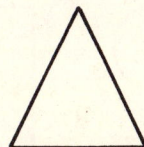 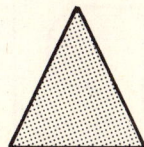 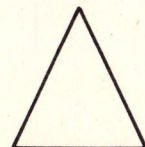 

A	A	I	H	A	A
C	D	O	C	C	G
O	Q	O	O	C	D
U	U	W	V	U	U
M	M	A	M	N	W
P	R	D	P	P	R
S	Z	S	S	J	U
E	E	L	F	E	H
J	U	J	I	J	A
B	P	B	B	D	B

41

o	o	a	e	c	o
a	a	p	d	a	o
e	c	e	e	o	e
g	d	g	p	q	g
s	z	s	z	s	s
f	l	f	k	t	f
h	b	h	h	d	n
l	j	i	l	l	i
k	x	k	k	x	h
m	r	m	m	n	h

I I I I I I I I I I I I

I

L L L L L L L L L L L

L

T T T T T T T T T

T

I   T   I   T   I
L   I   L   I   T
T   L   I   L   L

I I

I I

43

O O O O O O O O O

O

Q Q Q Q Q Q Q Q Q

Q

C C C C C C C C C

C

G G G G G G G G G

G

O O

C C

44

U U U U U U U U U

U

J J J J J J J J J

J

S S S S S S S S S

S

U	J	U	J	U	S
J	S	J	U	S	J
S	U	S	S	U	J

S S

U U

D D D D D D D D D D

D

P P P P P P P P P

P

B B B B B B B B B

B

R R R R R R R R R

R

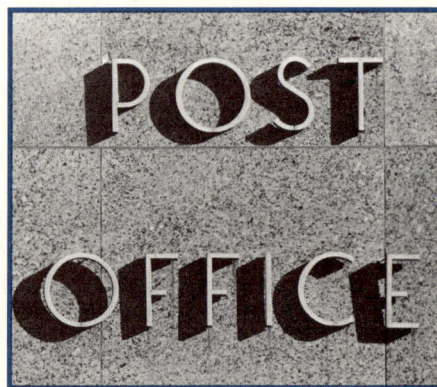

BANK

POST

F F F F F F F F F F F

F

E E E E E E E E E E E

E

H H H H H H H H H H H

H

E	H		H	E
F	F		E	H
H	E		F	F

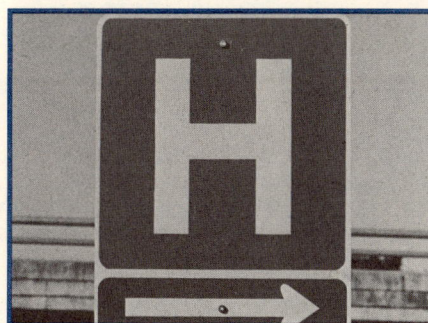

E E

H H

47

M M M M M M M M M M M M M

M

N N N N N N N N N N

N

V V V V V V V V V V V

V

W W W W W W W W W W

W

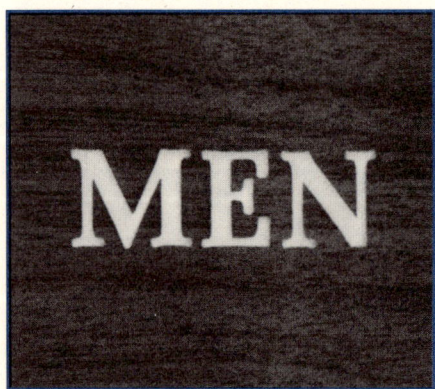

MEN

NO

X X X X X X X X X

X

Y Y Y Y Y Y Y Y Y

Y

A A A A A A A A A

A

Z Z Z Z Z Z Z Z Z

Z

K K K K K K K K K

K

K	K	K	Y	Z	K
A	Z	A	A	X	Y

49

i i i i i i i i i i i i i i

i

j j j j j j j j j j j j j

j

l l l l l l l l l l l l l

l

t t t t t t t t t t t t t

t

in

out

in

out

50

b b b b b b b b b b

b

d d d d d d d d d d

d

p p p p p p p p p p

p

q q q q q q q q q q

q

closed

d d

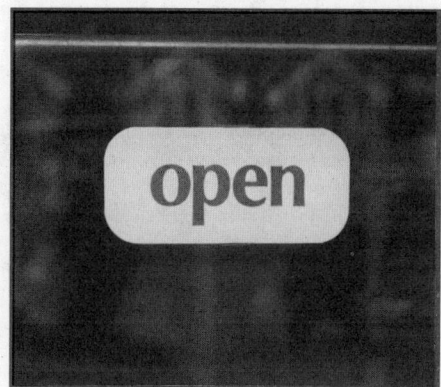

open

p p

h h h h h h h h h h h h

h

n n n n n n n n n n n n

n

m m m m m m m m m m m m

m

r r r r r r r r r r r r

r

help wanted

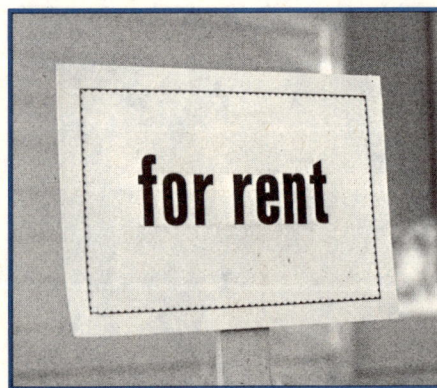

for rent

help

rent

o　o　o　o　o　o　o　o　o　o

o

a　a　a　a　a　a　a　a　a　a

a

c　c　c　c　c　c　c　c　c　c

c

e　e　e　e　e　e　e　e　e　e

e

exit

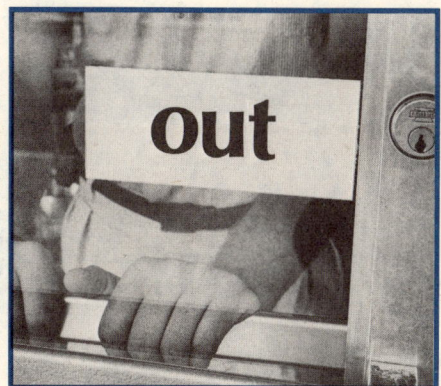

out

53

g g g g g g g g g g g

g

f f f f f f f f f f f

f

s s s s s s s s s s s

s

u u u u u u u u u u u

u

for sale

no smoking

f f

s s

54

X X X X X X X X X X X

X

V V V V V V V V V V V

V

W W W W W W W W W W W

W

y y y y y y y y y y y

y

Z Z Z Z Z Z Z Z Z Z Z

Z

k k k k k k k k k k k

k

M M T T U U

S S X X B B

C C O O R R

c c d d f f

h h g g k k

o o s s t t

A Y H

I W D

N P Z

a x y

j m p

u w z

Aa Bb Cc Dd Ee Ff Gg Hh Ii
Jj Kk Ll Mm Nn Oo Pp Qq Rr
Ss Tt Uu Vv Ww Xx Yy Zz

Aa Aa _____ _____ _____ _____

Bb Bb _____ _____ _____ _____

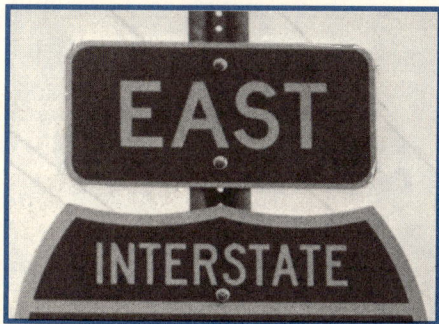

A

a

B

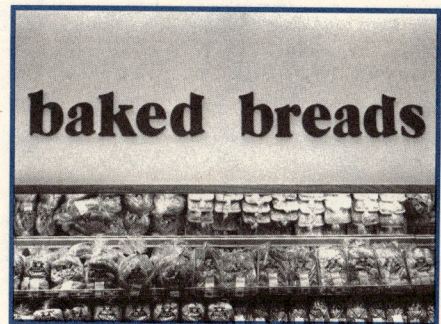

b

Aa Bb **Cc Dd** Ee Ff Gg Hh Ii

Jj Kk Ll Mm Nn Oo Pp Qq Rr

Ss Tt Uu Vv Ww Xx Yy Zz

Cc Cc

Dd Dd

C

c

D

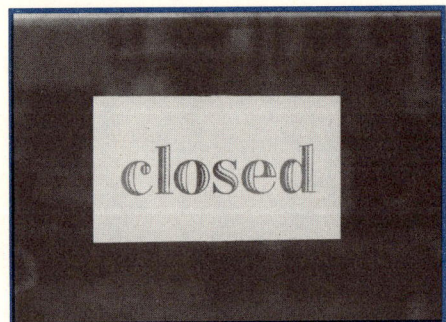

d

Aa Bb Cc Dd Ee Ff Gg Hh Ii
Jj Kk Ll Mm Nn Oo Pp Qq Rr
Ss Tt Uu Vv Ww Xx Yy Zz

Ee Ee ___ ___ ___
Ff Ff ___ ___ ___

E

e

F

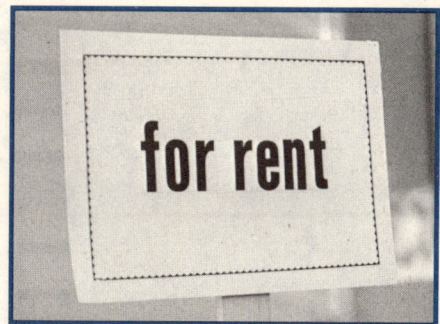

f

Aa Bb Cc Dd Ee Ff Gg Hh Iı
Jj Kk Ll Mm Nn Oo Pp Qq Rr
Ss Tt Uu Vv Ww Xx Yy Zz

Gg Gg —————————————
Hh Hh —————————————

G

g

H

h

A
a
c
e

B
d
b
c

C
e
c
a

D
d
f
b

E
a
c
e

F
d
b
f

G
i
g
j

H
h
l
k

Aa Bb Cc Dd Ee Ff Gg Hh Ii
Jj Kk Ll Mm Nn Oo Pp Qq Rr
Ss Tt Uu Vv Ww Xx Yy Zz

Ii Ii

Jj Jj

I

i

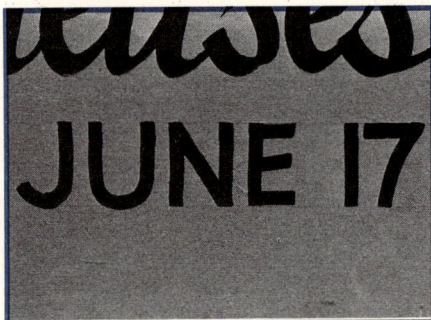

J

j

Aa Bb Cc Dd Ee Ff Gg Hh Ii
Jj Kk Ll Mm Nn Oo Pp Qq Rr
Ss Tt Uu Vv Ww Xx Yy Zz

Kk   Kk ‑ ‑ ‑ ‑ ‑ ‑ ‑ ‑ ‑ ‑
Ll   Ll ‑ ‑ ‑ ‑ ‑ ‑ ‑ ‑ ‑ ‑

K

k

L

l

Aa Bb Cc Dd Ee Ff Gg Hh Ii
Jj Kk Ll Mm Nn Oo Pp Qq Rr
Ss Tt Uu Vv Ww Xx Yy Zz

Mm Mm
Nn Nn

M

m

N

n

Aa Bb Cc Dd Ee Ff Gg Hh Ii
Jj Kk Ll Mm Nn Oo Pp Qq Rr
Ss Tt Uu Vv Ww Xx Yy Zz

Oo Oo ___ ___ ___ ___

Pp Pp ___ ___ ___ ___

O

o

P

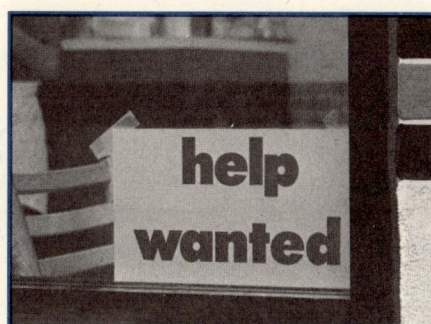

p

I

j
l
i

J
j

g
i
j

K

k
h
l

L

h
l
k

M

n
m
r

N

m
r
n

O

n
o
p

P

p
q
o

Aa Bb Cc Dd Ee Ff Gg Hh Ii
Jj Kk Ll Mm Nn Oo Pp Qq Rr
Ss Tt Uu Vv Ww Xx Yy Zz

Qq Qq
Rr Rr

Q

q

R

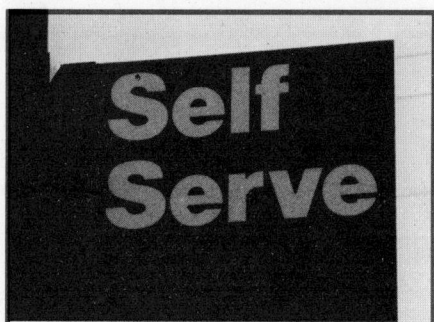

r

Aa Bb Cc Dd Ee Ff Gg Hh Ii
Jj Kk Ll Mm Nn Oo Pp Qq Rr
Ss Tt Uu Vv Ww Xx Yy Zz

Ss   Ss
Tt   Tt

S

s

T

t

Aa Bb Cc Dd Ee Ff Gg Hh Ii
Jj Kk Ll Mm Nn Oo Pp Qq Rr
Ss Tt Uu Vv Ww Xx Yy Zz

Uu Uu
Vv Vv

NO U
TURN

U

out

u

NO
VACANCY

V

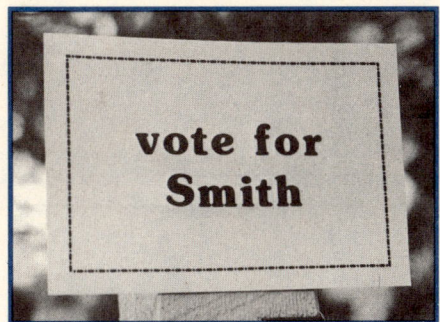

vote for
Smith

v

Aa Bb Cc Dd Ee Ff Gg Hh Ii
Jj Kk Ll Mm Nn Oo Pp Qq Rr
Ss Tt Uu Vv Ww Xx Yy Zz

Ww Ww _____ _____ _____

Xx Xx _____ _____ _____

W

w

X

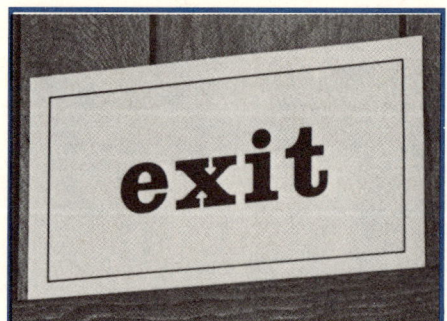

x

	o		n
Q	q	R	r
	p		m
	z		t
S	s	T	x
	x		y
	w		v
U	u	V	u
	v		y
	v		s
W	w	X	y
	x		x

Aa Bb Cc Dd Ee Ff Gg Hh Ii
Jj Kk Ll Mm Nn Oo Pp Qq Rr
Ss Tt Uu Vv Ww Xx Yy Zz

Yy Yy
Zz Zz

Y

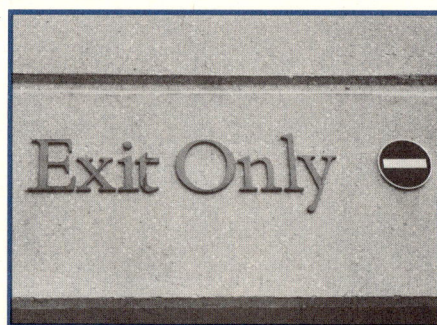

y

Z

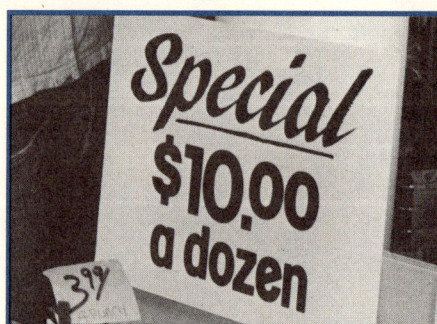

z

R

n
r
q

H

p
h
s

N

n
o
m

G
H
Q

g

I

L
M
P

A

b
a
o

F

e
f
g

e

E
F
O

q

Q
O
P

| r
|
|

R
P
J

h

H
N
I

| D
|
|

d
p
b

Z

z
o
s

| B
|
|

b
d
e

A B C D E F G H I

J K L M N O P Q R

S T U V W X Y Z

a b c d e f g h i j k l m

n o p q r s t u v w x y z

A B

Y Z

a b

y z

A B C d

e F G h

I j K L M

n o p Q r

S T U v

w X Y Z

ALPHABET

A _____

_____ Z

A ⌢_____   _____⌢ D   G ⌢_____   _____⌢ K   _____⌢ O

S ⌢_____   _____⌢ U   E ⌢_____   _____⌢ J   L ⌢_____

P ⌢_____   _____⌢ S   V ⌢_____   Y ⌢_____   _____⌢ Y

_____⌢ C   F ⌢_____   I ⌢_____   _____⌢ M   _____⌢ H

_____⌢ B   _____⌢ Q   N ⌢_____   W ⌢_____   _____⌢ T

---

a _____

_____ z

---

b ⌢_____   u ⌢_____   n ⌢_____   _____⌢ l   _____⌢ s

_____⌢ w   y ⌢_____   s ⌢_____   q ⌢_____   _____⌢ p

f ⌢_____   _____⌢ e   a ⌢_____   o ⌢_____   _____⌢ m

h ⌢_____   _____⌢ j   l ⌢_____   t ⌢_____   w ⌢_____

d ⌢_____   c ⌢_____   _____⌢ v   _____⌢ x   k ⌢_____

77

? ?

! !

. .

, ,

How are you ?

Hello .

Yes , I am.

Watch out !

?	What is your name ?
!	Be careful !
.	There it is .
,	No , I am not.

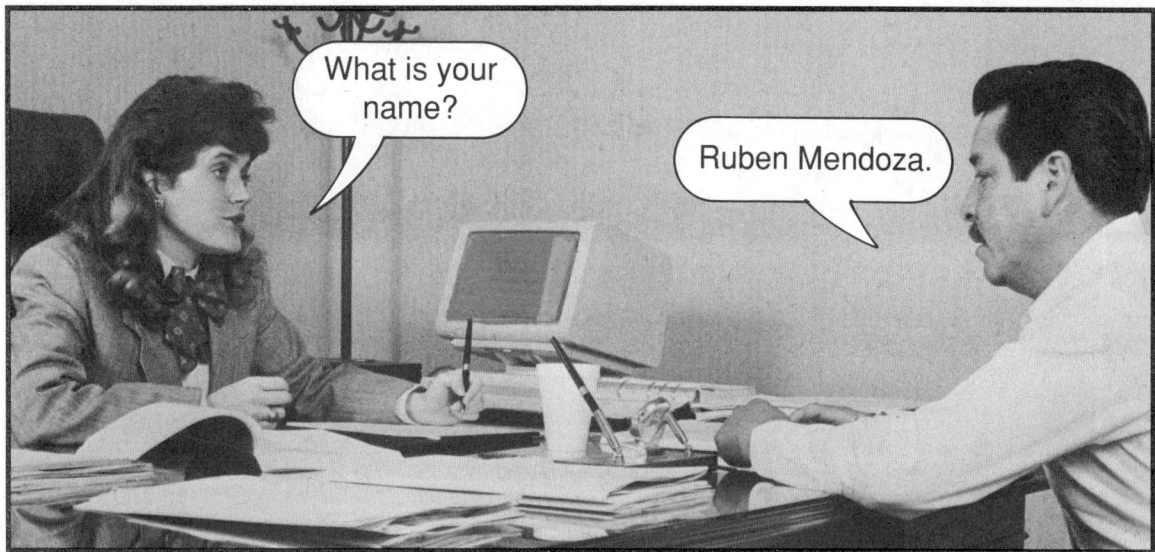

What is your name?_____

What is your name?_____

What is your name?_____
print

_____
name

_____
name

_____
name (please print)

What is your first name?_____

What is your first name?_____

_____
first name

_____
first name

What is your last name?_____

What is your last name?_____

_____
last name

_____
surname

What is your middle name? _____

What is your middle initial? _____

_____

What is your name?_____

What is your name?_____

print

_____

name (please print)

_____

| last name | first name | middle initial |

_____

| last name | first name | middle initial |

Sign your name here.

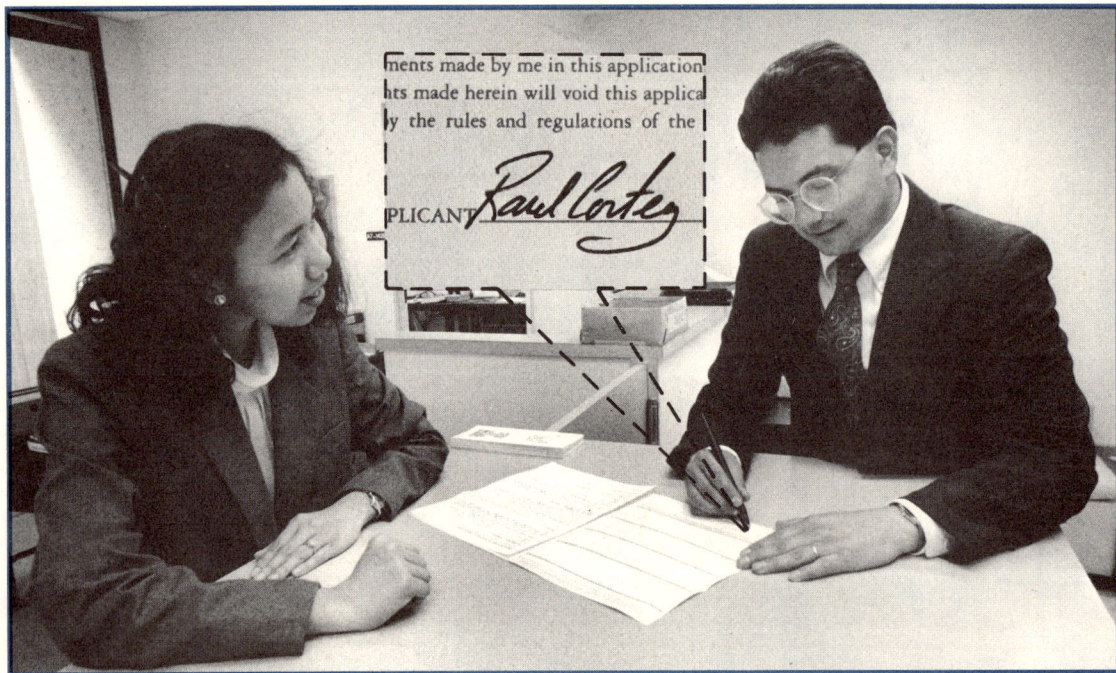

ments made by me in this application
hts made herein will void this applica
ly the rules and regulations of the

PLICANT *Paul Cortez*

_____

signature

_____

signature

_____

sign here

_____

sign here

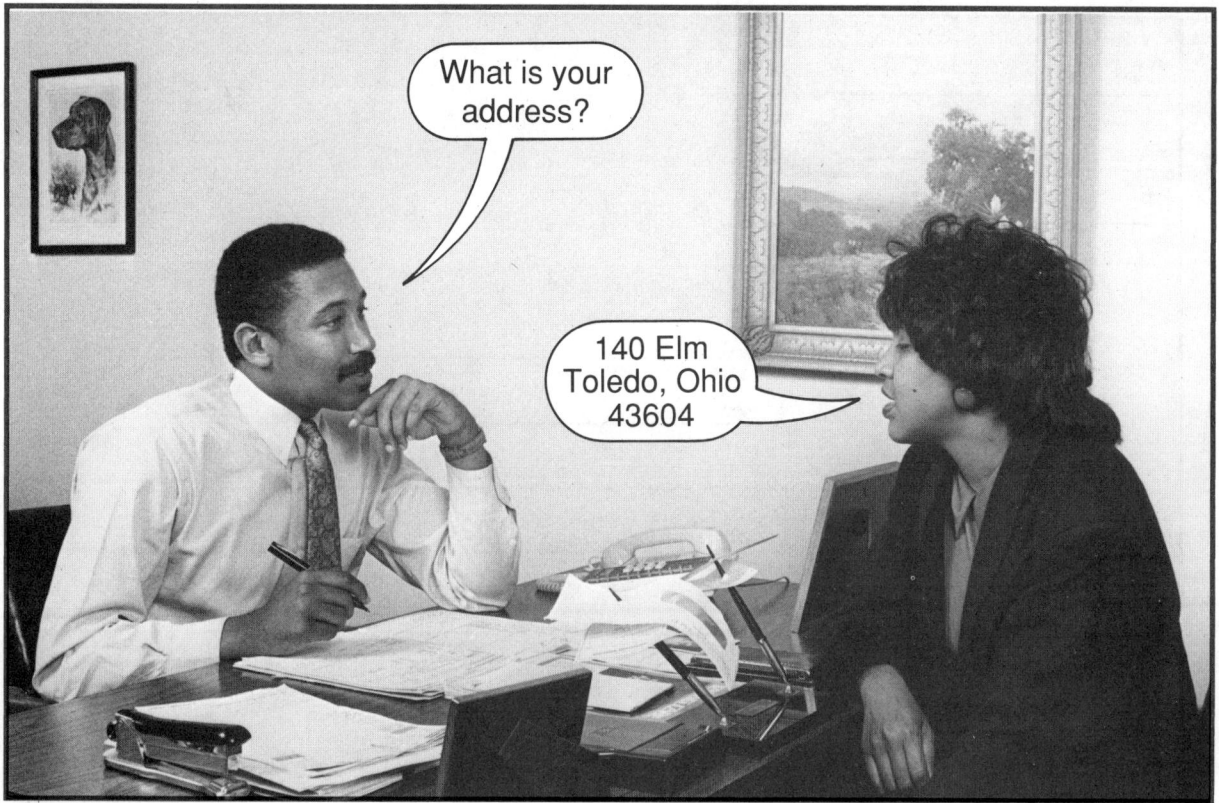

What is your address? _____

_____

What is your address? _____

_____

What is your address? _____

_____

_____
street

_____
city   state   zip code

_____
street   apt. no.

_____
city   state   zip code

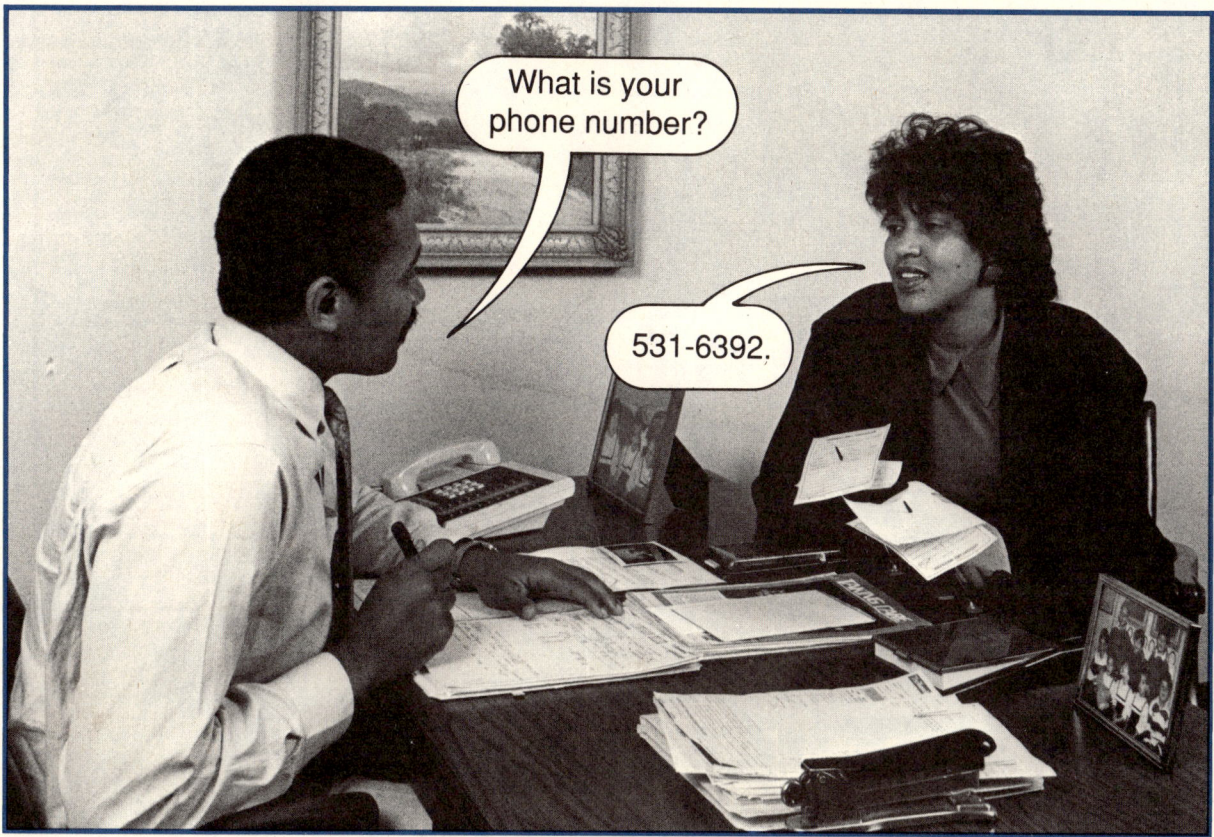

What is your phone number? □□□ - □□□□

What is your phone number? □□□ - □□□□

What is your telephone number? _____

What is your telephone number? _____

What is your phone number and your area code?

(□□□) □□□ - □□□□

What is your phone number and your area code?

(□□□) □□□ - □□□□

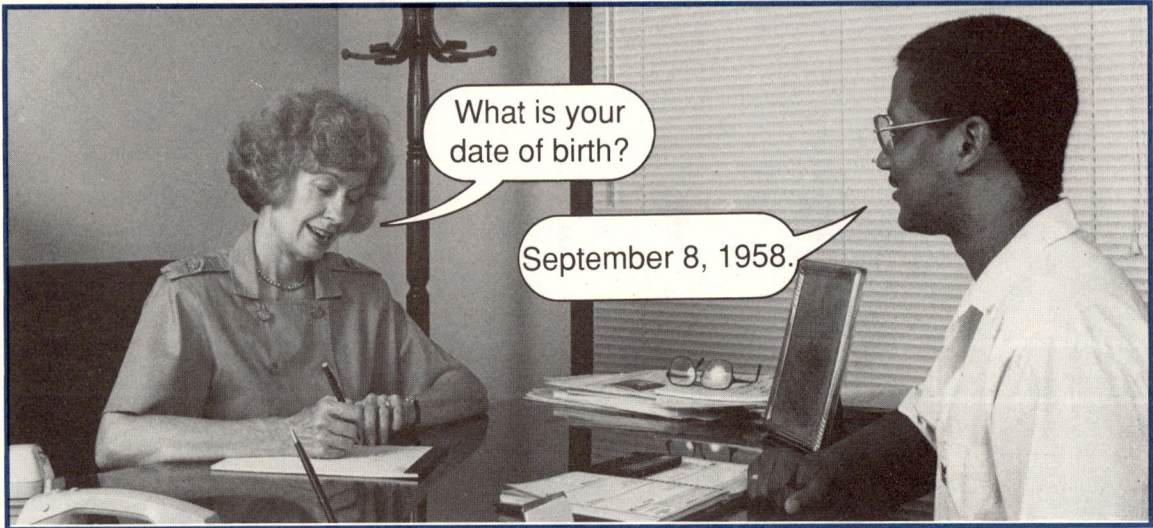

Date of Birth _____|_____|_____
                     Month   Day   Year

Date of Birth _____|_____|_____
                     Month   Day   Year

_____   _____
       date of birth   date of birth

_____   _____
        birthdate   birthdate

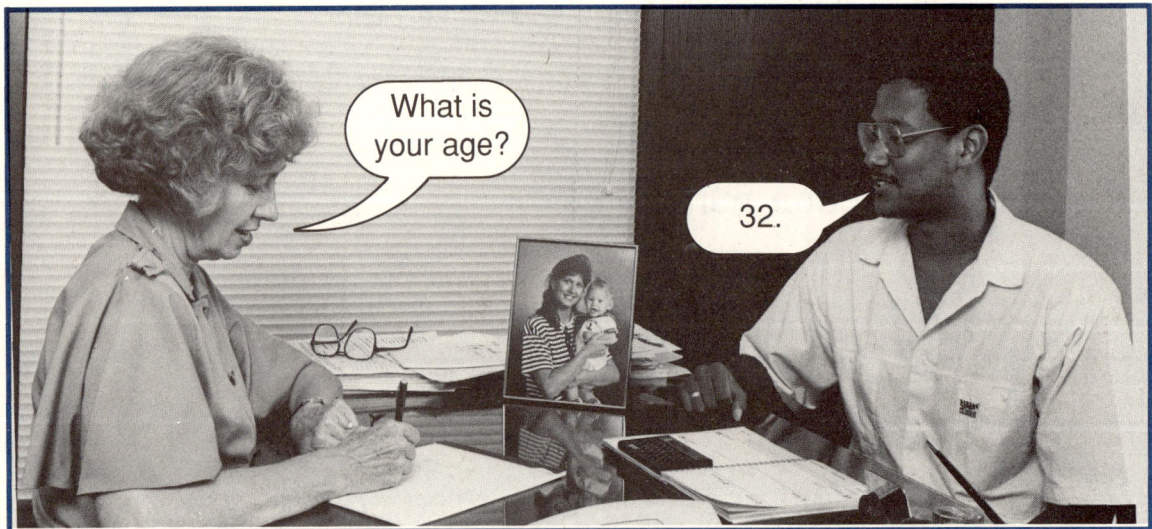

What is your age? _____   Age _____

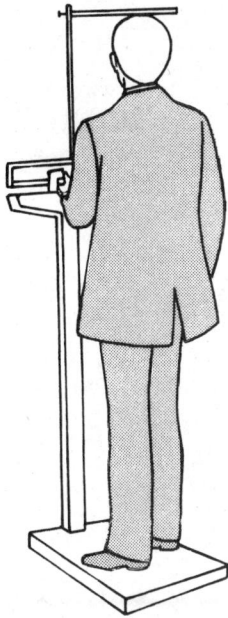

height
5 ft. 10 in.

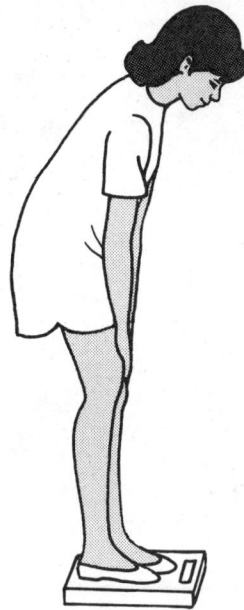

weight
110 lbs.

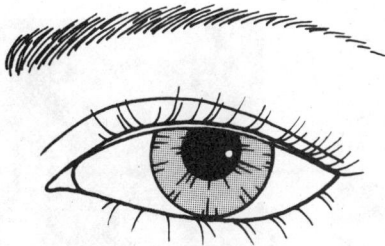

color of eyes

brown	green	blue

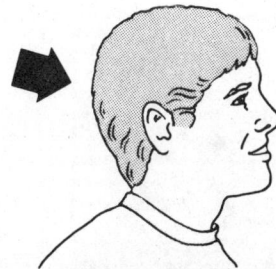

color of hair

black	brown	red	blond

_____ lbs.
weight

_____ ft. _____ in.
height

_____ lbs.
weight

_____ ft. _____ in.
height

brown	green	blue
←

_____
color of eyes

black	brown	red	blond
←

_____
color of hair

SEX

☐ male
☐ female

SEX

☐ M
☐ F

male
M

female
F

married

single
divorced
widowed
separated

single
divorced
widowed
separated

Marital Status

☐ single
☐ married
☐ widowed

☐ divorced
☐ separated

Mr.

Miss
Mrs.
Ms.

Miss
Ms.

Mrs. Gonzalez

Mr. Walker

Miss Jones

Mr. Mrs. Miss Ms._____

name

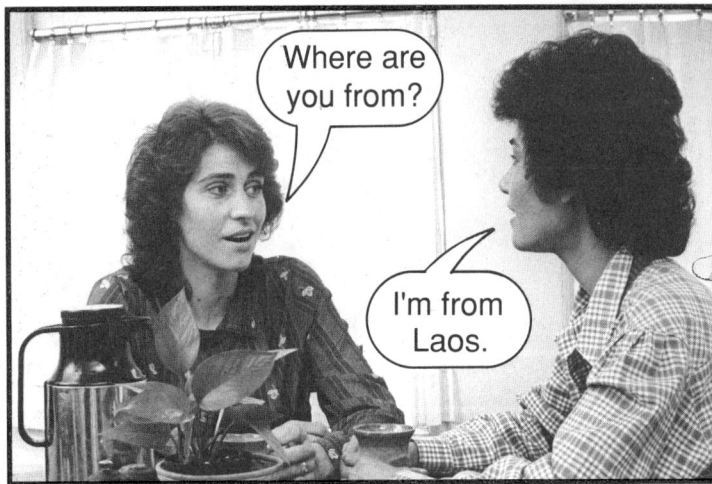

Where are you from? _____

Where are you from? _____

Where are you from? _____

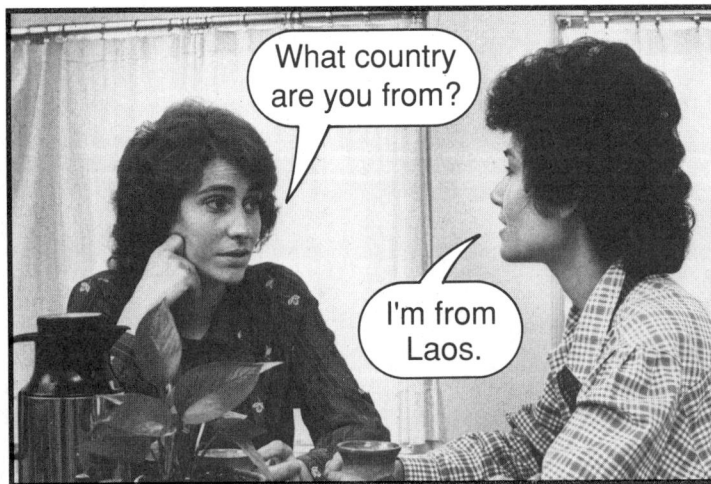

_____
country

_____
country

_____
native country

_____
birthplace

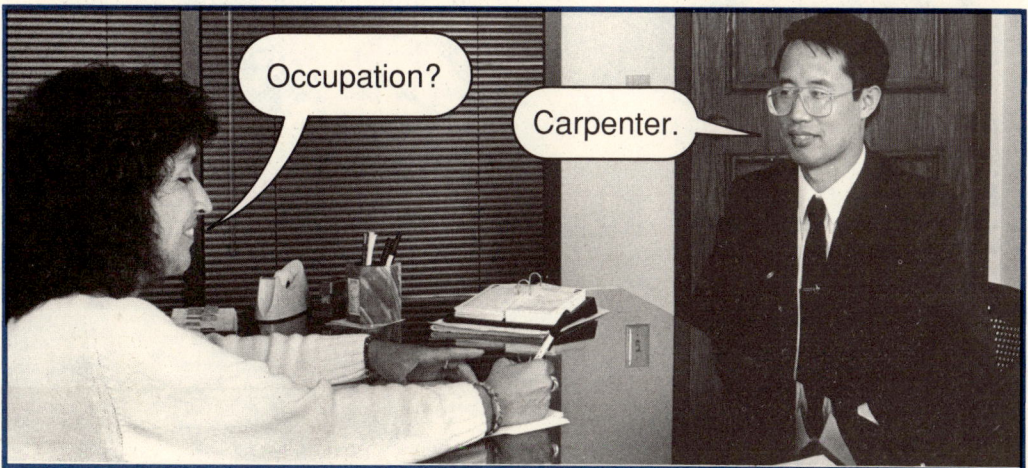

---

spouse's name   no. of children

---

occupation

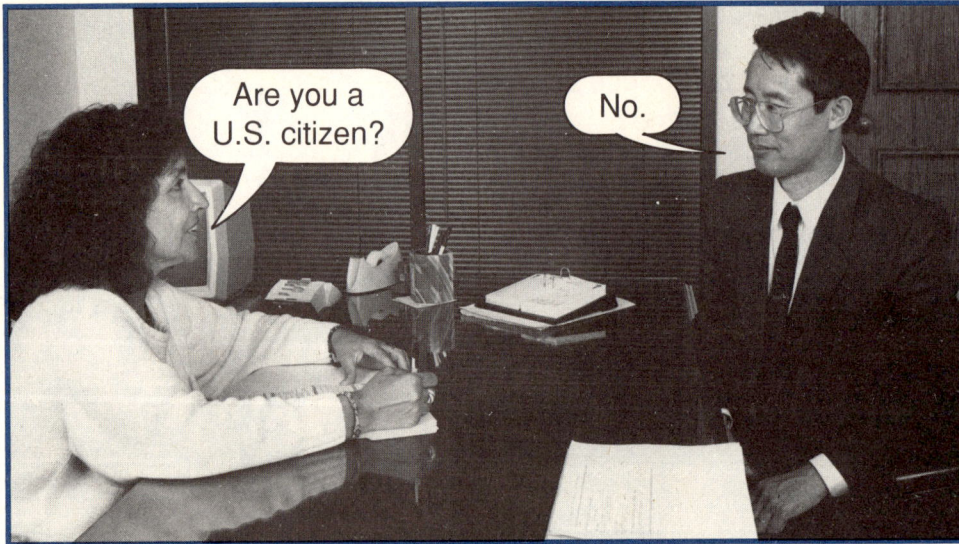

Are you a U.S. citizen?   yes ☐   no ☐

U.S. citizen?   yes ☐   no ☐

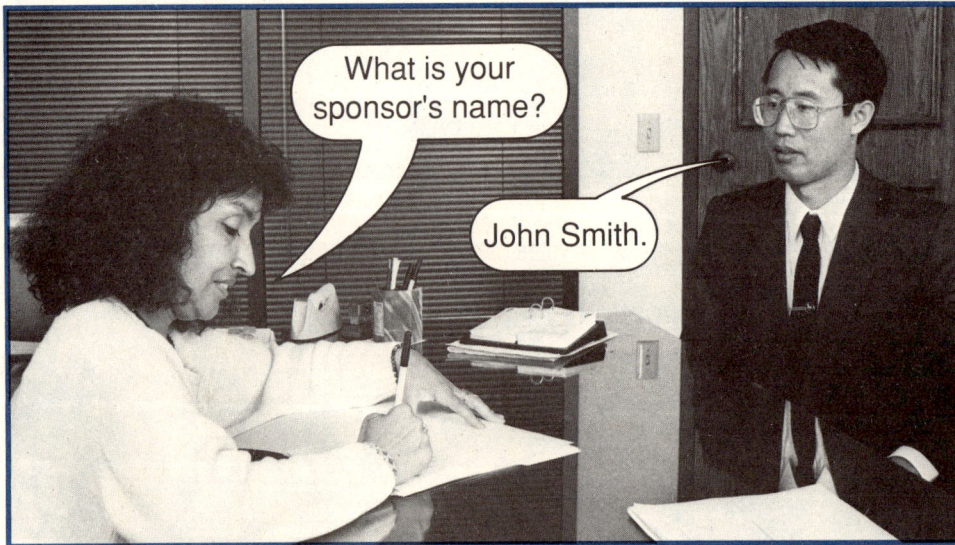

_____
native country

_____   _____
alien number   date of entry

_____   _____
sponsor's name   sponsor's phone

_____
sponsor's address

Name _____
                last   first   middle initial

Spouse's name _____
                    last   first   middle initial

Address _____
                        street

_____
            city   state   zip code

Phone (_____) _____ – _____

Social Security Number _____ – ____ – _____

Date of Birth _____

Age _____

Sex ☐ M   ☐ F

Height _____ ft. _____ in.

Weight _____ lbs.

No. of children _____

Occupation _____

Are you a U.S. citizen?   ☐ yes   ☐ no

Birthplace _____

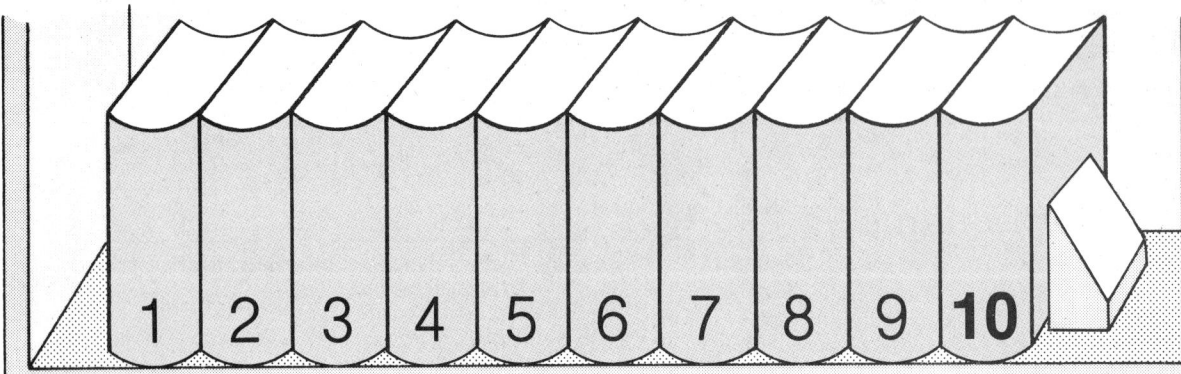

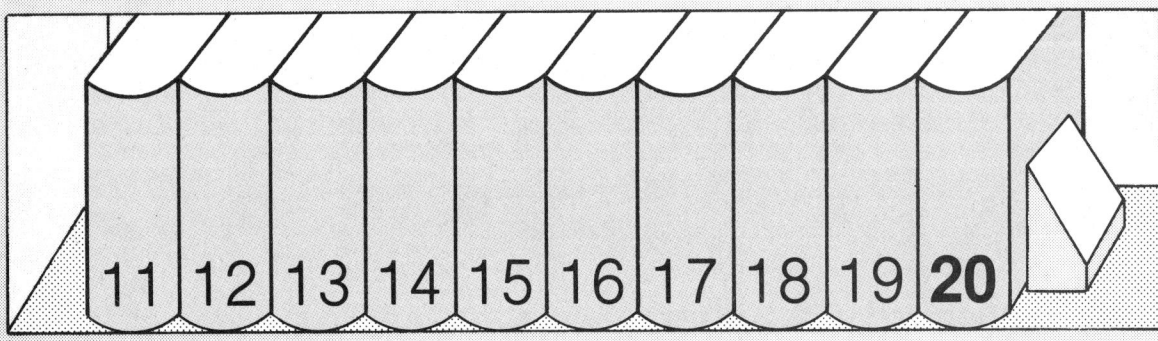

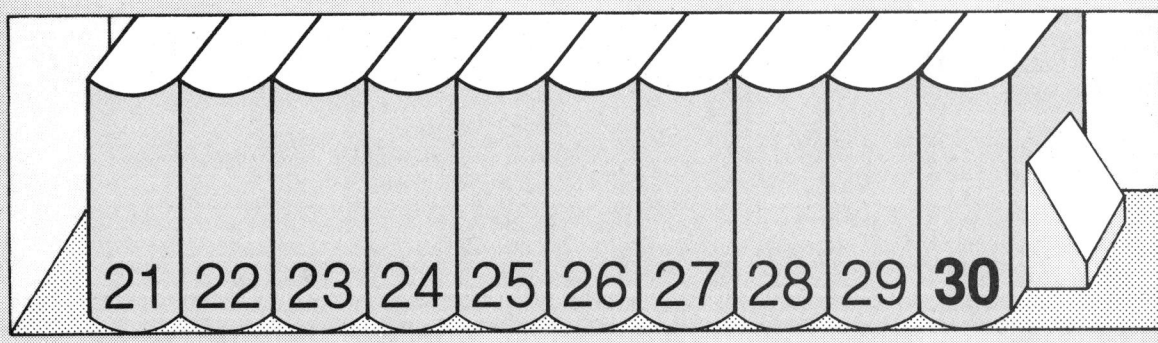

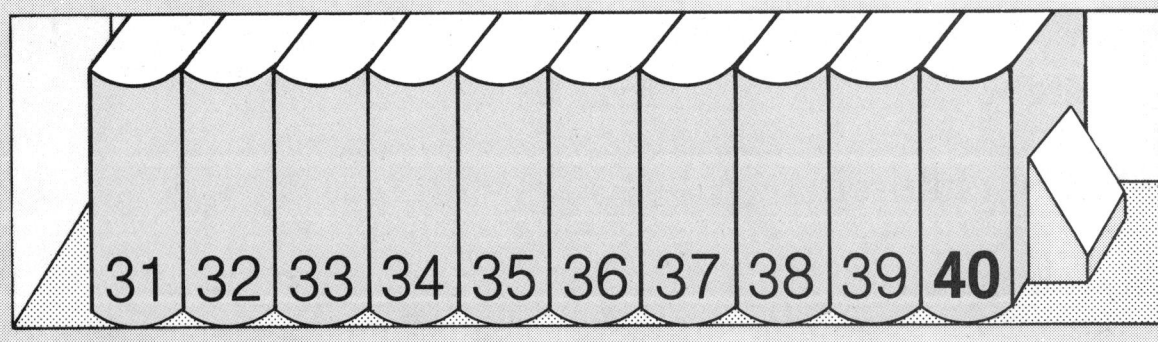

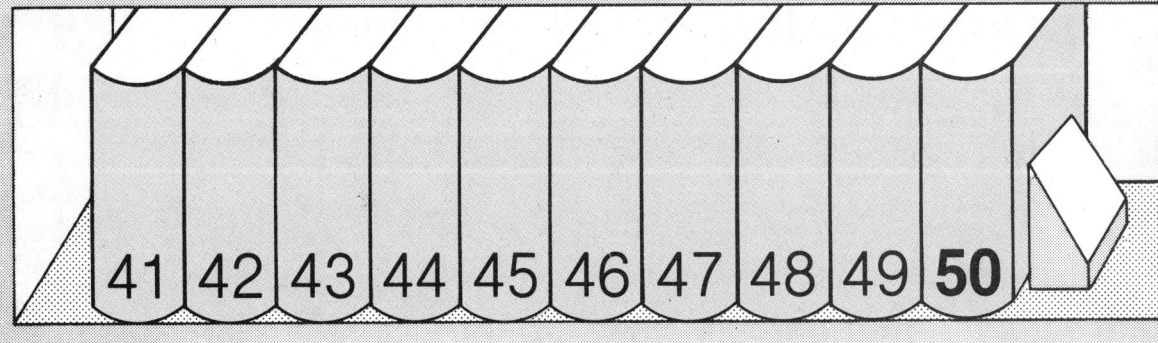

| 51 | 52 | 53 | 54 | 55 | 56 | 57 | 58 | 59 | **60** |

| 61 | 62 | 63 | 64 | 65 | 66 | 67 | 68 | 69 | **70** |

| 71 | 72 | 73 | 74 | 75 | 76 | 77 | 78 | 79 | **80** |

| 81 | 82 | 83 | 84 | 85 | 86 | 87 | 88 | 89 | **90** |

| 91 | 92 | 93 | 94 | 95 | 96 | 97 | 98 | 99 | **100** |

1	2		4	5		7		9	10
	12		14	15	16		18	19	
21		23	24		26			29	30
31	32			35	36	37		39	40
41		43	44				48	49	
51	52		54		56				60
	62	63		65			68		
71			74	75		77	78		80
81	82		84		86	87		89	90
91		93		95			98	99	

1 ———————————————————————————————— 10

11 ——————————————————————————————— 20

21 ——————————————————————————————— 30

31 ——————————————————————————————— 40

41 ——————————————————————————————— 50

51 ——————————————————————————————— 60

61 ——————————————————————————————— 70

71 ——————————————————————————————— 80

81 ——————————————————————————————— 90

91 ——————————————————————————————— 100

1	2	3	4	5	6	7	8	9	10
	12	13		15	16	17		19	20
21		23	24		26	27	28		30
31	32		34	35		37	38	39	
41		43		45	46	47		49	50
	52	53	54			57	58		60
61		63	64	65		67		69	
71	72			75	76		78		80
	82	83	84			87		89	
91			94	95	96		98		100

¢ ¢

$ $

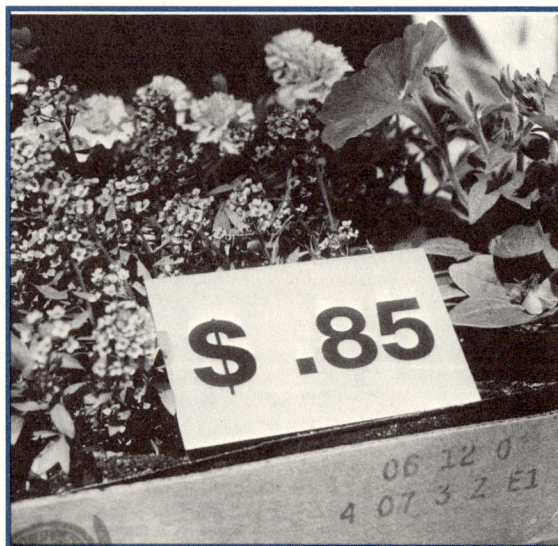

$	$5	36¢	$3.01	$.05
.	88¢	$7	$.09	$11.13
¢	69¢	$3.05	$6	33¢
$	$7	$7.30	$.08	79¢
¢	$.13	$4.50	65¢	1¢

1¢ _____

5¢ _____

10¢ _____

25¢ _____

50¢ _____

$1.00 _____

1¢ ——————————— 1 penny

5¢
5 pennies

1 nickel

10¢
10 pennies

1 dime

25¢

25 pennies

1 quarter

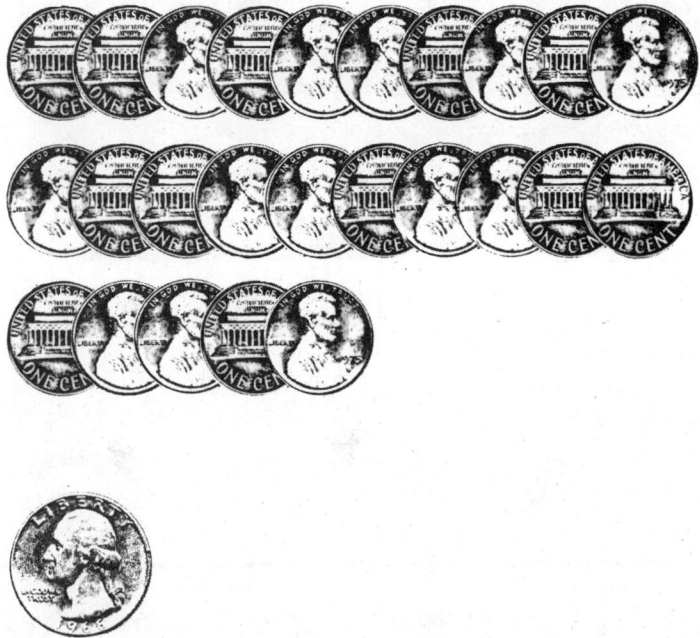

50¢

50 pennies

1 half dollar

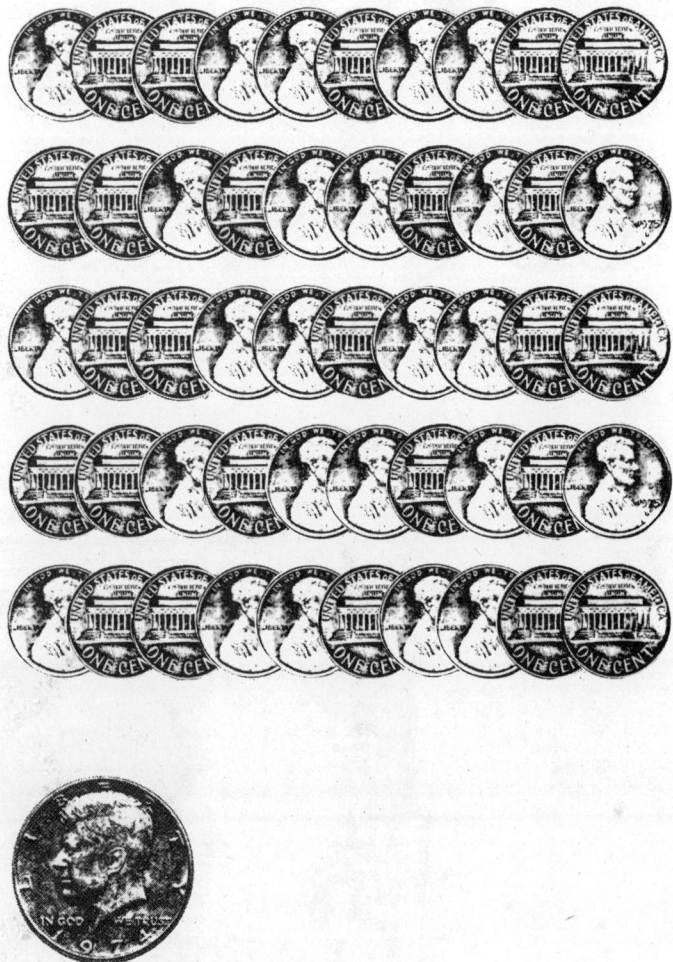

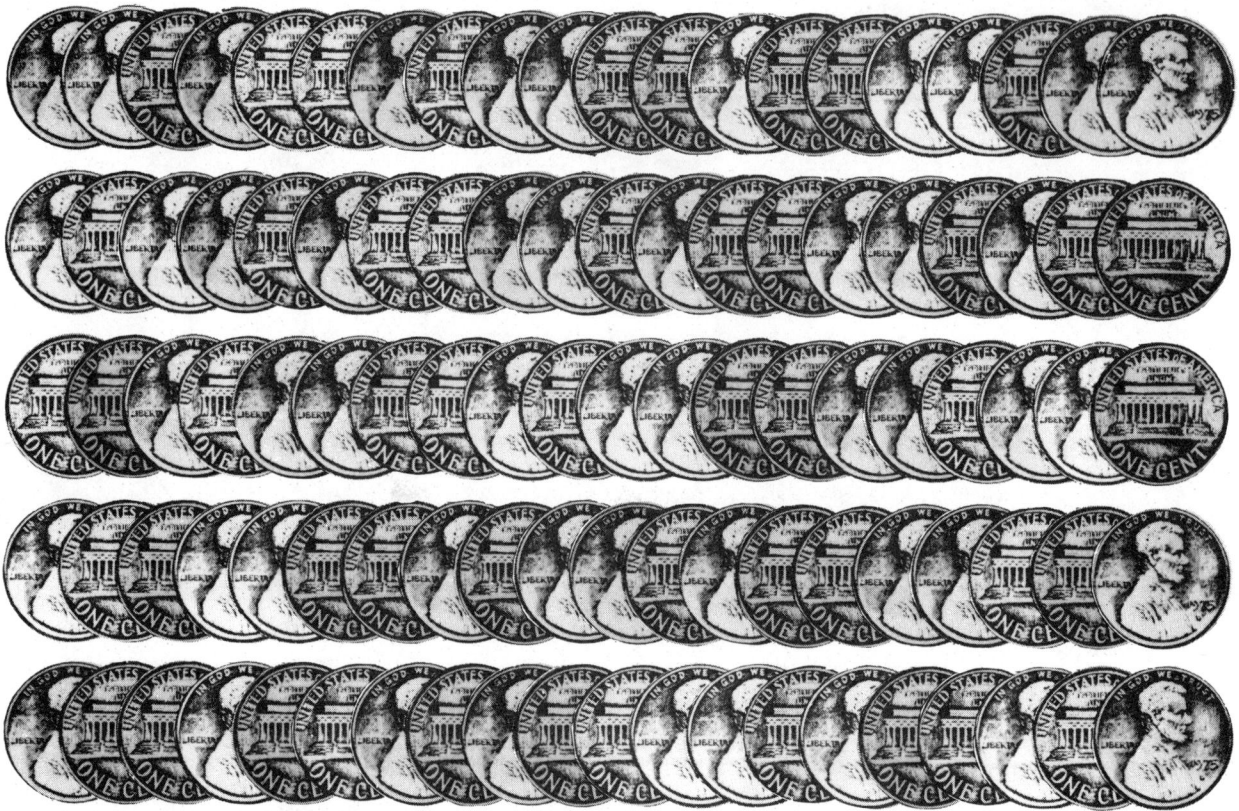

100 pennies

$1.00

1 dollar

1 penny	= 1¢ =	$.01
1 nickel	= 5¢ =	$.05
1 dime	= 10¢ =	$.10
1 quarter	= 25¢ =	$.25
1 half dollar	= 50¢ =	$.50
1 dollar	= 100¢ =	$1.00

37¢ = _____   15¢ = _____   75¢ = _____

40¢ = _____   5¢ = _____   19¢ = _____

50¢ = _____   4¢ = _____   65¢ = _____

25¢ = _____   8¢ = _____   80¢ = _____

30¢ = _____   7¢ = _____   70¢ = _____

42¢ = _____   16¢ = _____   83¢ = _____

$.06 = _____ $.76 = _____ $.22 = _____

$.36 = _____ $.30 = _____ $.81 = _____

$.25 = _____ $.07 = _____ $1.00 = _____

$.49 = _____ $.18 = _____ $ .75 = _____

$.64 = _____ $.03 = _____ $ .20 = _____

$.11 = _____ $.02 = _____ $ .50 = _____

How much is it?

It's 75¢.

It's 45¢.

It's 50¢.

How much is it?

It's 30¢.

It's 45¢.

It's 15¢.

How much is it?

It's 30¢.

It's 15¢.

It's 16¢.

How much is it?

It's 25¢.

It's 35¢.

It's 27¢.

How much is it?

It's 70¢.

It's 65¢.

It's 85¢.

How much is it?

It's 42¢.

It's 57¢.

It's 37¢.

$13 60

$9 15

$15 50

$8 95

$13 75

$16 75

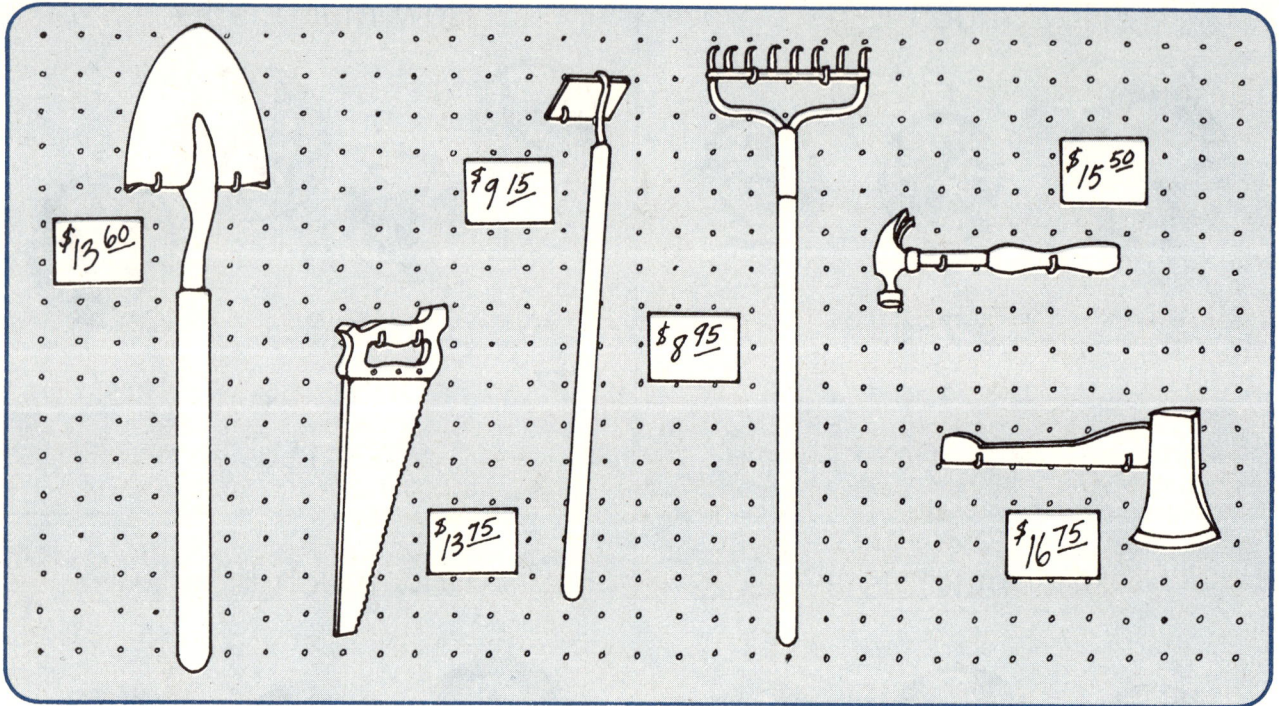

How much is the ? _____

How much is the ? _____

How much is the ? _____

How much is the ? _____

How much is the ? _____

How much is the ? _____

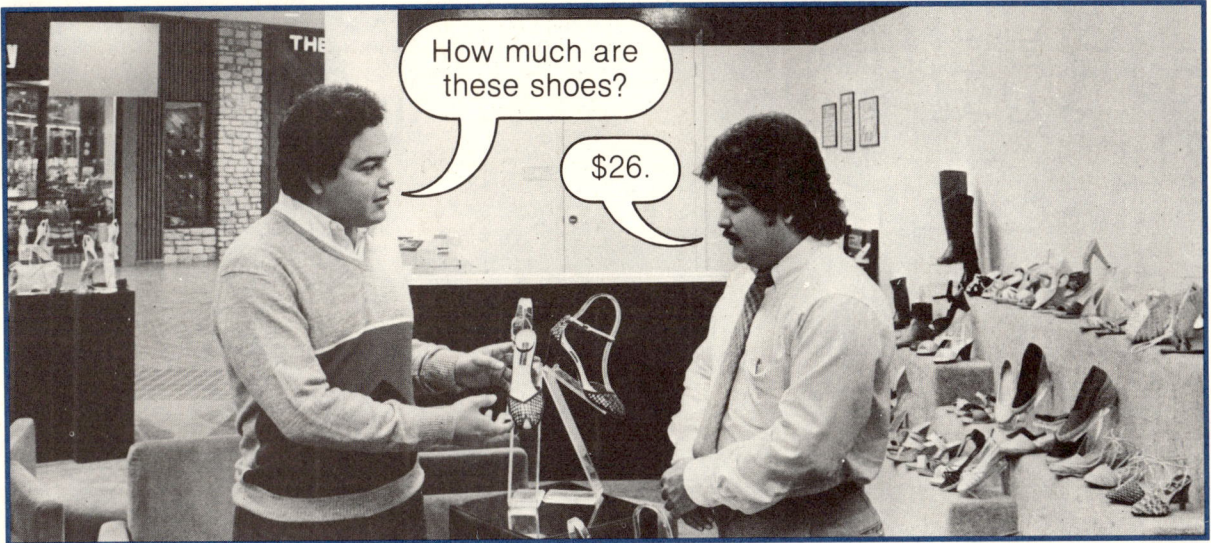

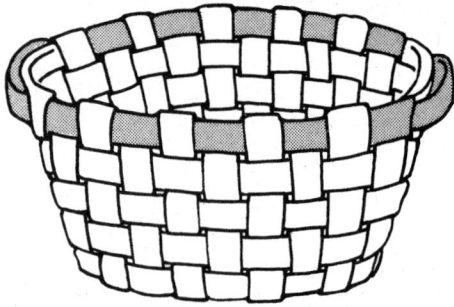

$1.89

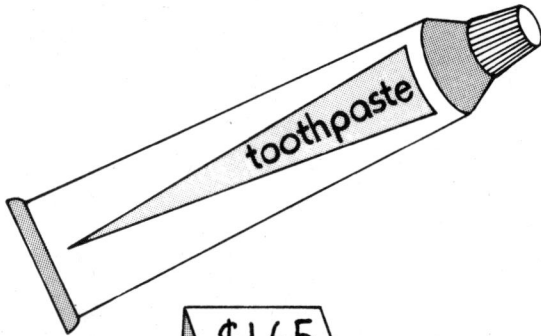

$1.65

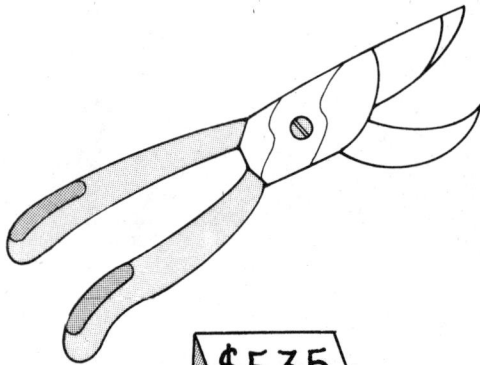

$5.35

MILK

$1.15

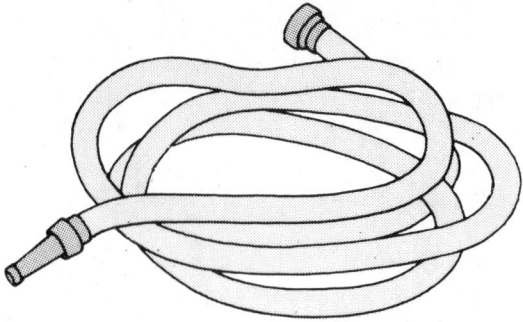

$6.85

$8.75

$26.15

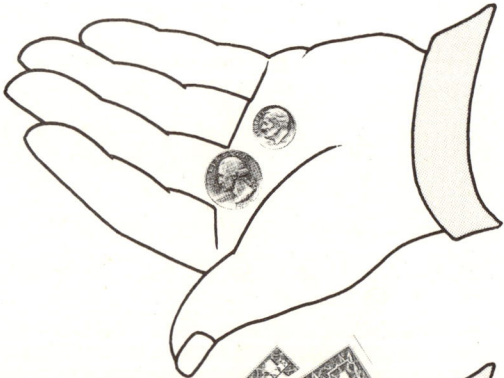

How much is your change?

_____

How much is your change?

_____

How much is your change?

_____

1¢

10¢

25¢

$1.00

5¢

$5.60

$1.40

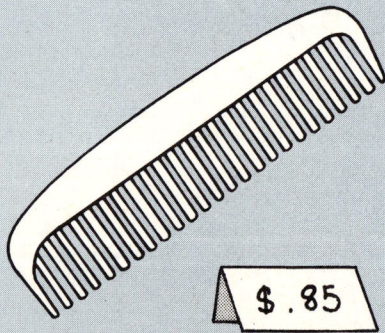

$.85

$8.77

FIRE

_____

DOCTOR

_____

AMBULANCE

_____

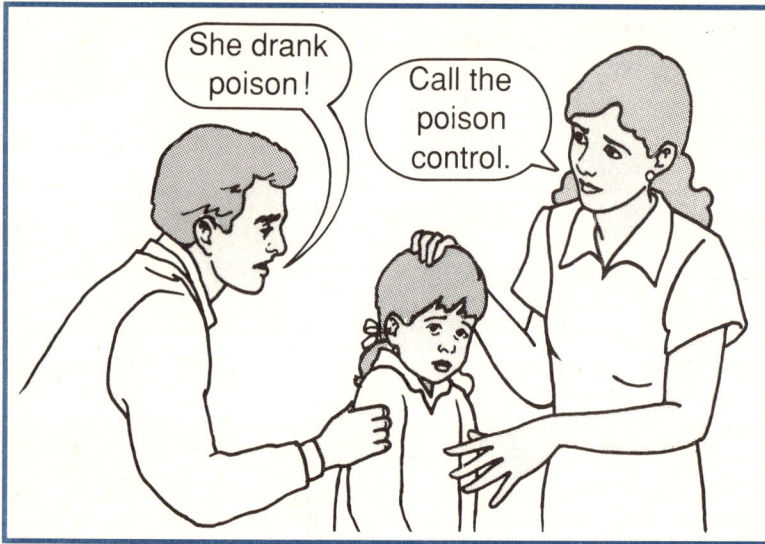

POISON CONTROL

_____

POLICE

_____

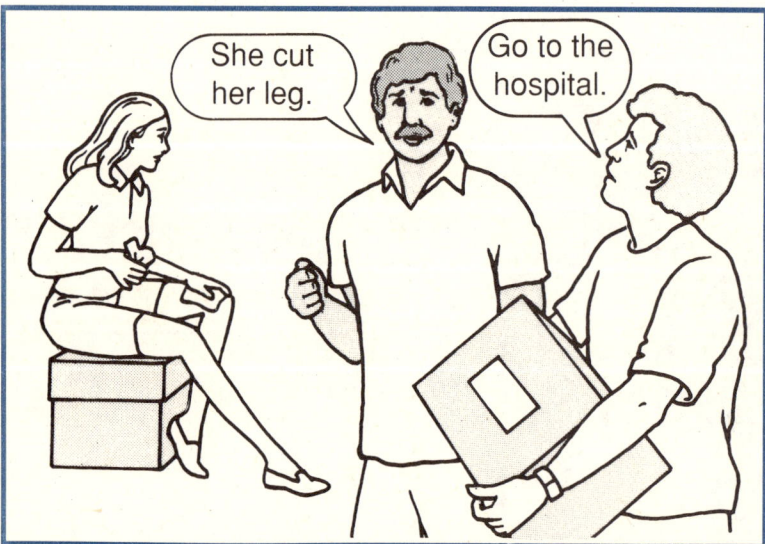

HOSPITAL

_____

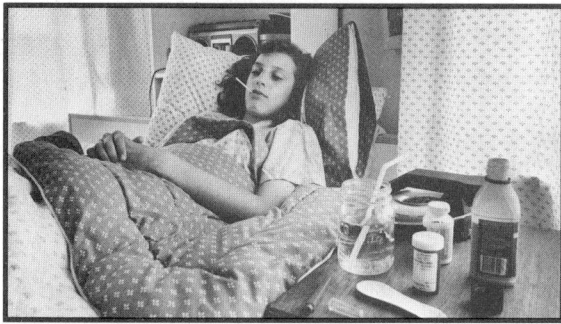

POISON
CONTROL

AMBULANCE

POLICE

FIRE
DEPARTMENT

DOCTOR

NO
BICYCLES

WALK

DO NOT WALK

PHONE

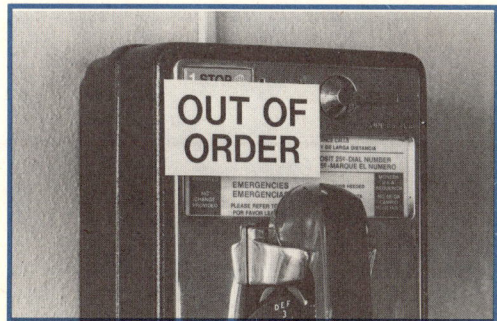

OUT OF ORDER

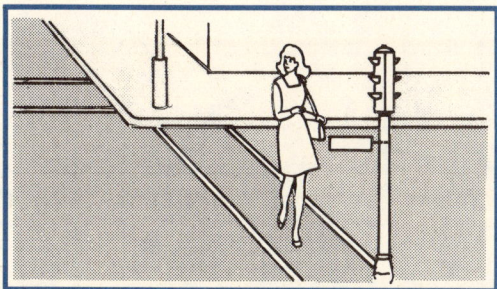

ENTER

EXIT

PUSH

PULL

PUSH

EXIT

PULL

NO
PARKING

DANGER

KEEP
OUT

NO SMOKING

REST ROOMS

MEN

WOMEN

HANDICAPPED

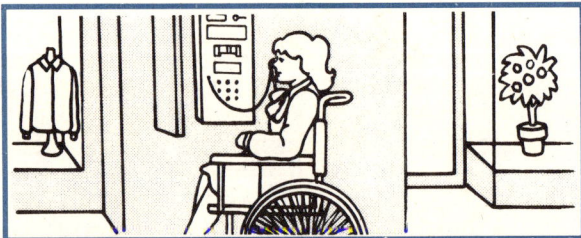

WOMEN

MEN

HANDICAPPED

OPEN

CLOSED

ON

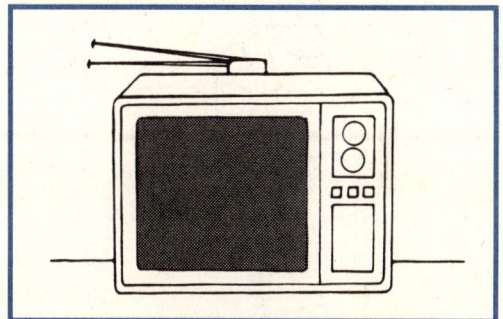

OFF

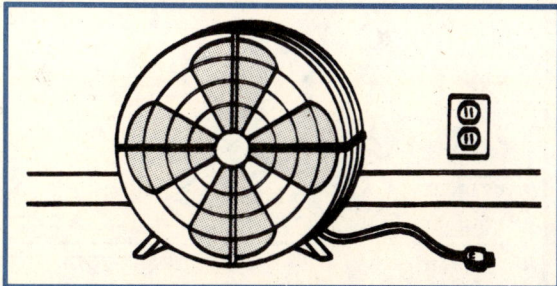

BUS STOP

SCHOOL

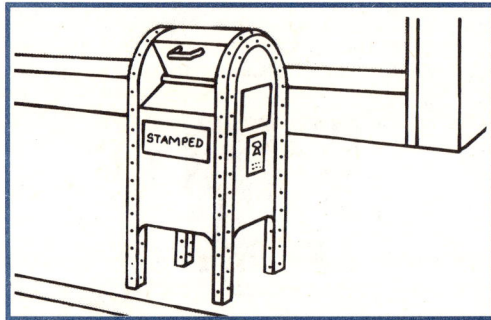

STAMPED

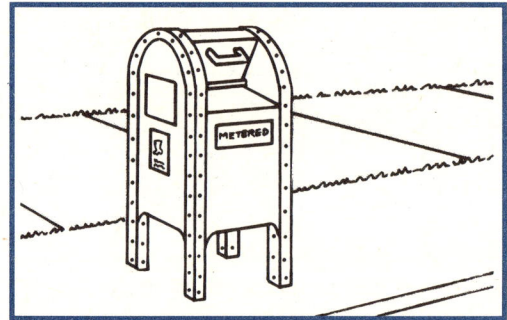

METERED

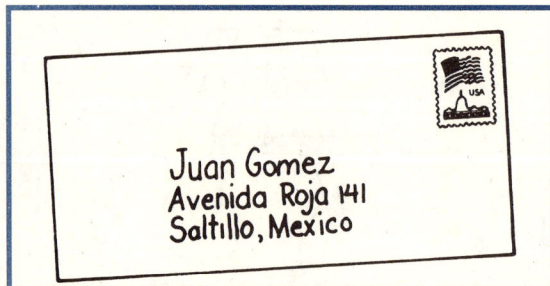

Juan Gomez
Avenida Roja 141
Saltillo, Mexico

BUS STOP

ENTER

FIRE
DEPARTMENT

POLICE

WALK

ON

NO SMOKING

DO NOT WALK

CLOSED

PULL   **ON**

 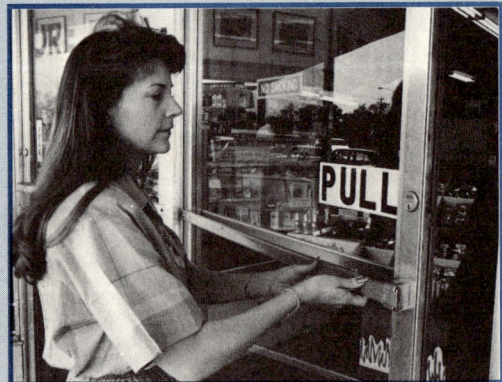